Independent Schools
Examinations Board

GEOGRAPHY
ISEB Revision Guide
(Fourth edition)

Belinda Froud-Yannic

Edited by Simon Lewis

Independent Schools
Examinations Board

www.galorepark.co.uk

GALORE PARK

Published by Galore Park Publications Ltd
338 Euston Road, London, NW1 3BH
www.galorepark.co.uk

Design and typesetting Typetechnique
Printed by Charlesworth Press
ISBN: 978 1 907047 66 4

First edition published 2005
Second edition published 2007
Third edition published February 2008, reprinted May 2008,
September 2008, 2009, revised October 2009, reprinted 2010, 2011
Fourth edition published 2011, reprinted 2011, 2012, 2013, 2014

Details of other ISEB Revision Guides for Common Entrance, examination
papers and Galore Park publications are available at www.galorepark.co.uk

Front cover image of the Giant's Causeway, N. Ireland
© Derek Croucher/Alamy

About the author

Belinda Froud-Yannic has been Head of Geography at Thomas's School, Clapham since 2001. She formerly taught at Broomfield School, Southgate. In her spare time she enjoys pottery, walking up hills and skiing. She believes that Geography is a subject that everyone can enjoy due to its diversity of themes and that lessons should be fun and full of fieldwork.

Acknowledgements

I would like to dedicate this book to the pupils of Thomas's Clapham from 2001 to 2011. They have worked incredibly hard, achieving fantastic Common Entrance results and a huge percentage have reached the dizzy heights of Top Geographer status! Thanks go to them for their constant ideas on how the guide could be improved and updated. Finally, sincere thanks go to Simon Lewis, my editor.

Contents

Introduction

I hope that you find this guide as useful as the pupils of Thomas's Clapham have over the past ten years. Try to look after your guide; it will be a vital aid before your Common Entrance examination and will also be of use during lessons and for homework.

I have included some example Common Entrance questions (called sample questions) for you to try during your revision period. At the end of each chapter, there is a summary of what you should know on that subject and some questions to test yourself. (The answers to these questions and the sample questions are provided at the back of the book). There is also a table of words and phrases. These words and phrases are divided into those you need to know for the exam and those that it is useful for you to know.

Take your copy of this guide to all lessons and keep it with you as often as possible, so that you can make the most of any free time you have (on the bus, in the bath, etc.). Remember that a good way to learn global location is to test your friends and family. A Christmas global location quiz is always enjoyable; you may even shock your parents at how much you know (and how little they know)!

You may find it useful to make revision cards (see some suggestions in *Study Skills* by Elizabeth Holtom, published by Galore Park). Try to fit all of the information (in bullet point form or as mind maps) onto a card; add all of the necessary maps or diagrams. Make sure that you know the location of the examples.

If you are unsure of any topic area remember to ask your teacher for help.

I wish you the best of luck in all of your examinations and remember that you can be a Top Geographer!

Tips on revising

Get the best out of your brain

- Give your brain plenty of oxygen by exercising. If you feel fit and well, you will be able to revise effectively.

- Eat healthy food while you are revising. Your brain works better when you give it good fuel.

- Think positively. Give your brain positive messages so that it will want to study.

- Keep calm. If your brain is stressed it will not operate effectively.

- Take regular breaks during your study time.

- Get enough sleep. Your brain will carry on sorting out what you have revised while you sleep.

Get the most from your revision

- Don't work for hours without a break. Revise for 20–30 minutes then take a 5 minute break.

- Do good things in your breaks: listen to your favourite music, eat healthy food, drink some water, do some exercise and juggle. Don't read a book, watch TV or play on the computer; it will conflict with what your brain is trying to learn.

- When you go back to your revision, review what you have just learnt.

- Regularly review the facts you have learnt.

Get motivated

- Set yourself some goals and promise yourself a treat when the exams are over.

- Make the most of all the expertise and talent available to you at school and at home. If you don't understand something, ask your teacher to explain.

- Get organised. Find a quiet place to revise and make sure you have all the equipment you need.

- Use year and weekly planners (available for download from www.galorepark.co.uk) to help you organise your time so that you revise all subjects equally.

- Use topic and subject checklists (available for download from www.galorepark.co.uk) to help you keep on top of what you are revising.

Know what to expect in the exam

- Use past papers to familiarise yourself with the format of the exam.

- Make sure you understand the language examiners use.

Before the exam

- Have all your equipment and pens ready the night before.

- Make sure you are at your best by getting a good night's sleep before the exam.

- Have a good breakfast in the morning.

- Take some water into the exam if you are allowed.

- Think positively and keep calm.

During the exam

- Have a watch on your desk. Work out how much time you need to allocate to each question and try to stick to it.

- Make sure you read and understand the instructions and rules on the front of the exam paper.

- Allow some time at the start to read and consider the questions carefully before writing anything.

- Read all the questions at least twice. Don't rush into answering them before you have a chance to think.

- If a question is particularly hard move on to the next one. Go back to it if you have time at the end.

- Organise your time so that you have time to check your answers at the end.

Tips for the Geography exam

- Remember that you need to answer all the questions in all three sections.

- Look at the number of marks available, in order to assess how much to write.

- Remember that marks are given for the level of detail. If you answer the questions with a high mark allocation in bullet points, you must make sure that the bullet points include sufficient detail.

- Always read the questions carefully, underlining, circling or highlighting key words or phrases.

- Do not leave blanks. If you do not know the answer, take an educated guess. Wrong answers do not lose marks.

- Make sure that all diagrams are clearly annotated (labelled with explanations). There are certain diagrams which it is essential you know how to draw. These are clearly marked throughout this guide.

- Look carefully at the resources given, e.g. maps, graphs; they will help you answer the question. (Remember the 'line' on a climate graph is the temperature and the 'blocks' are the rainfall.)

- Include impressive **geographical terms** from the tables at the end of each chapter whenever possible.

- On page 3 you will find a list of command words used in the exam. Make sure you are familiar with the meaning of these words so that you complete the question exactly as directed.

For more tips on how to get the best from your revision and exams see *Study Skills* by Elizabeth Holtom, published by Galore Park.

Useful resources

Study Skills by Elizabeth Holtom, ISBN: 9781902984599

So you really want to learn Geography Book 1 by James Dale-Adcock,
ISBN: 9781902984728

So you really want to learn Geography Book 1 Answer Book by James Dale-Adcock,
ISBN: 9781902984735

So you really want to learn Geography Book 2 Second edition by James Dale-Adcock,
ISBN: 9781905735556

So you really want to learn Geography Book 2 Answer Book by James Dale-Adcock,
ISBN: 9781905735280

Revision Crosswords for Common Entrance and Scholarship Geography by Simon Lewis,
Download: D0316111

All available from Galore Park: www.galorepark.co.uk

Command words glossary

Make sure you completely understand these words. Cover up the definition with a sheet of paper in order to test yourself.

annotate	add descriptive explanatory labels
choose	select carefully from a number of alternatives
complete	finish, make whole
define	give an exact description of
describe	write down the nature of the feature
develop	expand upon an idea
explain	write in detail how something has come into being and/or changed
give	show evidence of
identify	find evidence of
list	put a number of examples in sequence
mark and name	show the exact location of and add the name
name	give a precise example of
select	pick out as most suitable or best
shade and name	fill in the area of a feature and add the name
state	express fully and clearly in words
study	look at and/or read carefully
suggest	propose reasons or ideas for something

These words are used in the scholarship exam:

discuss	present viewpoints from various aspects of a subject
elaborate	similar to **expand** and **illustrate**
expand	develop an argument and/or present greater detail on
illustrate	use examples to develop an argument or theme

Chapter 1: Weather and climate

The weather and the climate are two different things:

- **Weather** is the hour-to-hour, day-to-day condition of the atmosphere (wind speed, wind direction, temperature, humidity, sunshine, type of precipitation).

- **Climate** is the average weather conditions for an area over a long period of time. The climate is often shown on a climate graph.

1.1 Instruments

Various instruments are used to measure features of the weather.

Temperature

Temperature is measured in degrees centigrade by a **maximum** and **minimum thermometer**. During the day, the mercury or alcohol expands, pushing the metal pin higher on the scale. The opposite happens at night.

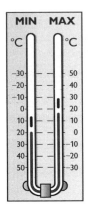

Fig. 1.1.1: Maximum and minimum thermometers

Digital thermometers can also be used to measure maximum and minimum temperatures.

Rainfall

Rainfall is measured in mm by a **rain gauge**. It is sunk into the ground away from shelter; the rim must be 30 cm above the ground to avoid splashing. The water collected can be poured into a measuring jug and the level recorded.

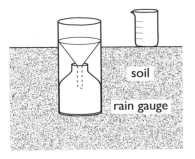

Fig. 1.1.2: Rain gauge

Air pressure

Air pressure is recorded on a **barograph** or **barometer**. As the weight of the air changes, the cylinder rises (or presses down) causing the lever to move and the pen to draw on the rotating drum.

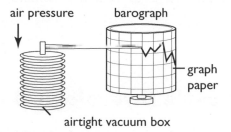

Fig. 1.1.3: Barograph

Wind

Wind is recorded by a **wind vane**, which shows the direction from which the wind blows. An **anemometer** measures wind speed. The wind makes a series of cups rotate. The velocity is measured in miles per hour or in knots.

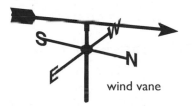
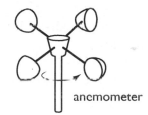

Fig. 1.1.4: Wind vane and anemometer

Stevenson screen

A **Stevenson screen** is a store where weather instruments are kept. It is white in order to reflect sunlight and slatted to allow air to circulate. It is placed above ground, on grass and away from buildings and trees.

Fig. 1.1.5: Stevenson screen

1.2 The water cycle (hydrological cycle)

Within the water cycle, water moves from one state to another. This drives our weather.

① The water cycle begins when water from the sea or a lake evaporates to form water vapour. Water from plants is also turned to water vapour by transpiration.

② This water vapour then rises, cools and condenses to form clouds.

③ As the clouds rise further and cool, precipitation will occur, in the form of rain, hail, snow or sleet.

④ Some of the water that falls is intercepted by the leaves on trees.

⑤ Some of the water will be stored on the surface (particularly if it is snow), will infiltrate into the soil or will flow over the land as surface run-off.

⑥ Some of the water which travelled as infiltration will move horizontally through the soil as throughflow.

⑦ Some of the water will move down through permeable rocks in a process called percolation.

⑧ Some of the water is stored as groundwater in porous rocks.

> You need to know how to draw this diagram.

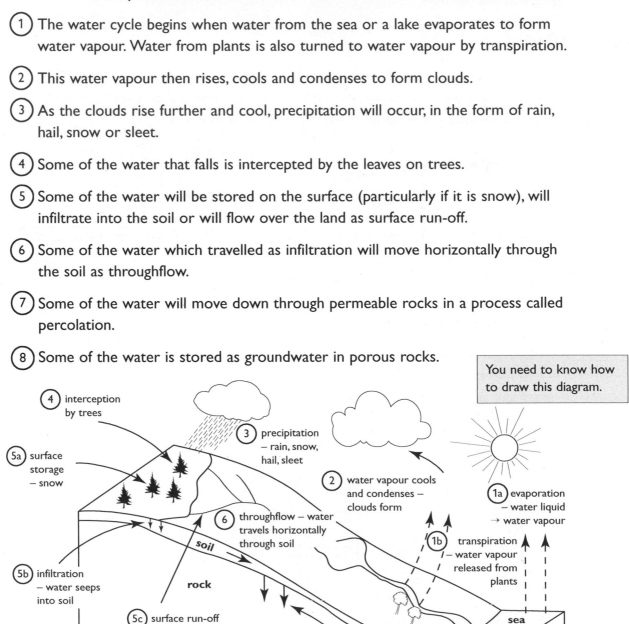

Fig. 1.2.1: The water cycle

1.3 Rainfall types

There are three main types of rainfall that are experienced in the UK: relief, convectional and frontal.

Relief rainfall

(1) Evaporation causes warm, moist air over the sea.

(2) As the air meets a hill, it is forced to rise.

(3) As it rises, the air cools and then condenses at dew point.

(4) Clouds form and rain falls.

(5) The air sinks over the other side of the hill. No rain falls here in the rainshadow.

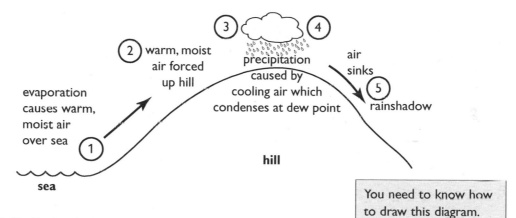

You need to know how to draw this diagram.

Fig. 1.3.1: Relief rainfall

Relief is the term used in Geography to describe the shape of the land.

Relief rainfall occurs in hilly or mountainous places, e.g. Wales, Scotland, the Alps and the Rockies.

Places at the foot of hills or mountains which do not face the prevailing wind are in the rainshadow and do not get very much rainfall.

Convectional rainfall

1. Hot sun heats any water on the ground.

2. Water from the ground is evaporated.

3. Water vapour rises, cools and condenses at dew point.

4. Clouds form and rain falls.

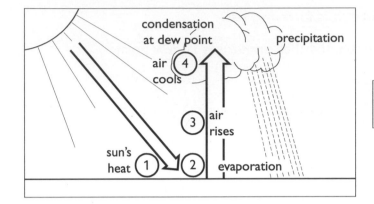

You need to know how to draw this diagram.

Fig. 1.3.2: Convectional rainfall

Convectional rainfall occurs in places that have strong sunshine and are relatively near a sea, lake or ocean.

Britain can experience convectional rain in the summer when it is very hot.

Tropical rainforests get convectional rain every day. The sun in the morning heats the puddles on the ground from the previous day's rain, then, by midday, it rains again.

Frontal rainfall

1. A warm air mass meets a cold air mass. The boundary where they meet is called a front.

2. Cold air is heavier, so it undercuts the warm air.

3. The warm air rises, cools and condenses at dew point.

4. Clouds form and it rains.

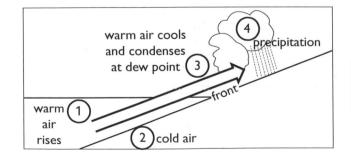

You need to know how to draw this diagram.

Fig. 1.3.3: Frontal rainfall

Frontal rain occurs in places where air masses from tropical areas and polar areas meet.

Britain receives much frontal rain.

When hot air and cold air meet, air pressure is low, as air is rising. This weather system is called a depression and brings very changeable weather.

1.4 Factors affecting temperature

There are a number of factors that affect temperature.

Latitude

The temperature rises as you get closer to the equator, and falls as you get closer to the Poles. This is because the sun's rays have further to travel to get to the Poles. For this reason, the south of Britain is warmer than the north.

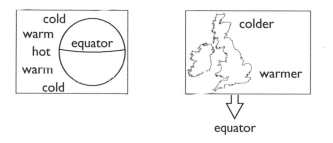

Fig. 1.4.1: Latitude

Altitude

The height of the land (the altitude) affects the temperature. The temperature falls by approximately 1°C for every 150 m you ascend.

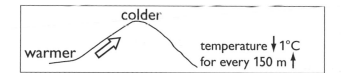

Fig. 1.4.2: Altitude

Distance from the sea

During the summer, the further inland you go, the warmer it gets, but during the winter, the opposite is true.

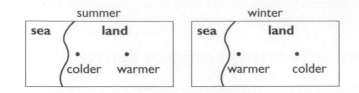

Fig. 1.4.3: Distance from the sea

The sea is very deep, so it takes a long time to heat up, but once it is hot it takes a long time to cool down. (Think of it being like a lasagne that takes a long time to cook, and then a long time to cool down.) The land is quick to heat up, but cools down quickly too. (It is like cheese on toast that just gets grilled on top and is quick to cook but cools down very quickly once you leave it on the table!)

Ocean currents

In the UK, the North Atlantic Drift and Gulf Stream means that the west side of the country is warmer than the east side.

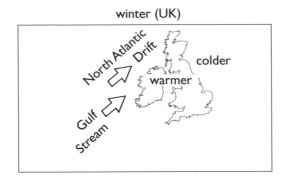

Fig. 1.4.4: Ocean currents

Prevailing wind direction

In the UK, the wind blows from the south-west for 80% of the time. This is a warm wind. When the wind blows from the south it is a warm/hot wind from Northern Africa. When the wind blows from the north it is a cold wind.

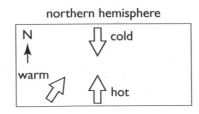

Fig. 1.4.5: Prevailing wind direction

1.5 A humid temperate climate (Britain)

Britain has a humid temperate climate. This means that it usually has warm summers and mild winters and rainfall throughout the year. The climate varies from one region to another.

North west

- mild summers (due to latitude)
- mild winters (due to ocean current)
- wet (due to relief and direction of prevailing wind)

North east

- mild summers (due to latitude)
- very cold winters (due to latitude)
- dry (as in rainshadow)

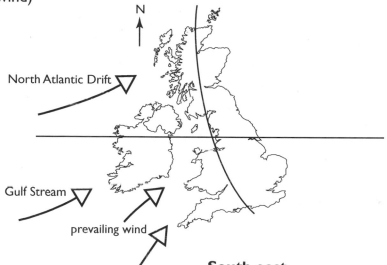

South west

- warm summers (due to latitude)
- mild winters (due to ocean current)
- wet (due to relief and direction of prevailing wind)

South east

- warm summers (due to latitude)
- cold winters (due to lack of effect of ocean current)
- dry (as in rainshadow)

Fig. 1.5.1: Britain's climate

The climate graph below shows the climate for a typical UK location. The blocks represent rainfall in mm and the line represents temperature in °C.

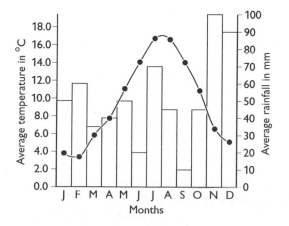

Fig 1.5.2: Climate graph for a typical UK location

The map below shows the average rainfall for Great Britain. This is a **choropleth map**. The areas coloured darkest have the most rainfall and those shaded a light colour have least rainfall.

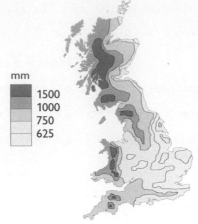

Fig 1.5.3: Rainfall map for Great Britain

1.6 A humid tropical climate

This is included for comparison but it is not part of the syllabus.

A humid tropical climate is experienced in equatorial regions of the world: West Africa, South East Asia, Northern Australia and South America, e.g. Amazonian rainforest in Brazil.

- Average annual rainfall is over 2000 mm.

- The range of temperature over the year is 1°C. The temperature is not seasonal.

The humid tropical climate is caused by:

- The equatorial location. The sun is therefore overhead for most of the year. The rays are concentrated on a small area causing high temperatures.

- Convectional rainfall. The sun in the morning evaporates the water. Storm clouds form and heavy rainstorms occur in the afternoon.

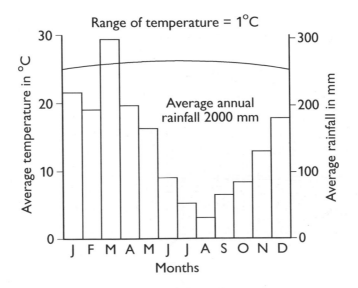

Fig 1.6.1: Climate graph for an equatorial region

1.7 Microclimates

A microclimate is the local climate of a small area. A number of factors affect microclimate:

- The physical features of the area, e.g. hills, lakes, valleys.
- The aspect of the area. This is the direction that a slope or wall faces; a south-facing slope is the warmest.
- The wind direction. In the UK, a northerly wind will be colder.
- Proximity to buildings. Buildings release heat and can provide shelter, thus increasing temperatures.
- The surface. Dark surfaces absorb heat.
- The distance from the sea. In winter, places near the sea are warmer than those further from the sea.

The microclimates in urban areas differ from those in rural areas.

An urban microclimate:

- is 1°C warmer than rural areas during the day. This is partly because man-made heat is released from power stations, houses, cars, etc.
- is 4°C warmer than rural areas at night. Tarmac absorbs heat during the day and releases it at night.
- experiences less wind than rural areas. Tall buildings act as wind breaks, but funnelling between buildings can cause gusts.
- has more convectional rainfall than rural areas because it is warmer than rural areas.
- has less snow.

A rural microclimate:

- is affected by the shape of the land. South-facing slopes are warmer and valley floors are cold at night due to cold air sinking (sometimes causing frosts).
- often experiences stronger winds because there is less shelter.

Sample questions

Try these sample questions. The answers are given at the back of the book.

Q. 1.4 The local atmospheric conditions in a small area, such as the grounds of a school, are called:
    (a) weather
    (b) precipitation
    (c) microclimate.   (1)

    1.5 Name three factors that may be very important in influencing the local climate (e.g. within the school grounds).   (3)

    1.6 Why might the local climate vary during the course of a bright, sunny day? (4)

Summary

You should now know the following:

1. The different instruments used to measure weather.

2. The process of the water cycle.

3. The different types of rainfall.

4. The different factors affecting temperature.

5. The reasons why temperature and rainfall vary across Britain.

6. The factors affecting microclimates.

Test yourself

Before moving on to the next chapter, make sure you can answer the following questions. The answers to questions 1–3 are at the back of the book.

1. (a) Name two factors that affect temperature.

    (b) What is the difference between weather and climate?

2. (a) What do geographers call the process of water sinking into soil?

    (b) What do geographers call the process of water travelling over the top of soil?

3. Write out each of these sentences using the correct word or words to finish the sentence:

    (a) Rain, hail, snow and sleet are all forms of
         infiltration   **precipitation**   **rainfall**   **weather system**

    (b) The prevailing wind direction for the UK is from the
         south-east   **north-west**   **south-west**   **north-east**

(c) The Gulf Stream is

an ocean current   a wind   a river   an island

(d) The Gulf Stream and North Atlantic Drift affect the south-west of the UK

in summer   all the year round   in spring   in winter

(e) Moist air forced to rise over upland areas causes

relief rainfall   frontal rainfall   convectional rainfall

4. Write the definitions of these words and phrases and then ask someone to check them.

Words you need to know	Words that will be useful
air mass	altitude
air pressure	anemometer
atmosphere	anticyclone
climate	aspect
condensation	barograph (barometer)
desert	climate graph
drought	convectional rainfall
equator	depression
evaporation	dew point
front	fog
hemisphere	frontal rainfall
humidity	ground water
infiltration	Gulf Stream
interception	humid temperate climate
irrigation	humid tropical climate
isotherm	isobars
microclimate	latitude
precipitation	maximum thermometer
vegetation	minimum thermometer
	North Atlantic Drift
	percolation
	prevailing wind
	rain gauge
	rain shadow
	relief rainfall
	seasonal
	shelter
	Stevenson screen
	surface run-off
	throughflow
	transpiration
	water cycle
	weather
	wind vane

Chapter 2: Landforms, weathering and erosion

In this chapter, you will be looking at the processes of weathering and erosion and how these create various landforms.

- **Weathering** is the breaking down of rocks by weather, plants and animals.

- **Erosion** is the wearing away and removal of rocks by rivers, sea, ice and wind.

2.1 Rock types

Weathering and erosion work at different speeds on different types of rock.

Igneous rock

This is formed from volcanic rock. If the magma cools underground, granite is formed. If it reaches the Earth's surface, it is called lava, which then forms basalt when it cools.

Sedimentary rock

This is formed when rivers transport particles of rock and remains of plants and animals to the sea. These then sink to the sea bed and, over millions of years, compress to form new rock.

Metamorphic rock

This is formed from sedimentary or igneous rock when it is exposed to extreme pressure or heat during the Earth's movements, e.g. chalk and limestone turn to marble; clay turns to slate.

2.2 Types of weathering

There are four main types of weathering: freeze-thaw weathering and onion-skin weathering (both physical) and chemical and biological weathering.

Physical weathering: freeze-thaw weathering

- This process starts when water seeps into cracks in the rock.

- At night the temperatures fall below 0°C, the water freezes and, as ice, expands.

- This forces the cracks open.

- The process happens again and again, and breaks up the rock.

- The loose rock is called scree.

Freeze-thaw is common in mountainous areas. Igneous rocks (granite) and metamorphic rocks (marble) from uplands are prone to this type of weathering.

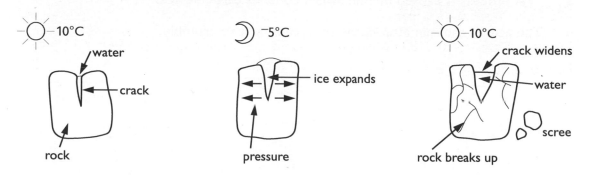

Fig. 2.2.1: Freeze-thaw weathering

Physical weathering: Onion-skin weathering or exfoliation

- This process happens when rocks are repeatedly subjected to heat and cold.

- Heat from the sun makes the outer layer expand.

- The cold at night makes the outer layer contract.

- The outer layer of the rocks then peels off.

- The loose rock is called scree.

- This type of weathering is common in desert areas, which are hot in the day and cool at night.

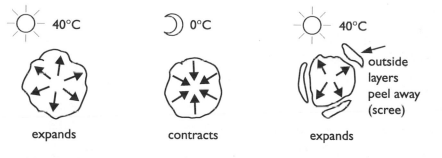

Fig. 2.2.2: Onion-skin weathering

Biological weathering

- This process is caused by plants and animals.

- Burrowing animals break up the rocks.

- Plant seeds fall into cracks and germinate, breaking up the rocks.

- Tree roots grow into cracks in the rocks and then exert pressure on the cracks as they grow, causing them to widen.

Chemical weathering

- This process is caused by rain, which contains carbonic acid.

- The acid in the rain attacks the rock, causing it to crumble.

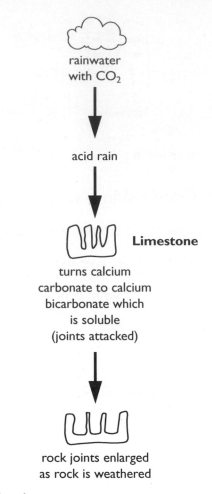

rainwater
with CO_2

↓

acid rain

↓

Limestone

turns calcium
carbonate to calcium
bicarbonate which
is soluble
(joints attacked)

↓

rock joints enlarged
as rock is weathered

Fig. 2.2.3: Chemical weathering

Sedimentary rocks, such as limestone and chalk, are particularly vulnerable to this type of weathering. As the carbonic acid falls on limestone, it turns it into calcium bicarbonate, which is soluble in water.

Limestone gravestones are commonly attacked and limestone pavements are also vulnerable as the acid water can seep into the grykes (deep cracks) and attack a large surface area.

2.3 Features of the river basin

The area of land drained by a river and its tributaries is called the **drainage** or **river basin**.

- The **watershed** is the edge of the river basin.

- The **source** is where the river starts.

- **Tributaries** are small streams or rivers than run into the main river channel.

- The **confluence** is the point where the tributary meets up with the main channel.

16

- A **meander** is a bend in the river.

- An **ox-bow lake** is where a meander has been cut off and a small lake has formed.

- The **flood plain** is the flat land in the lower course of the river, which is prone to flooding.

- The **estuary** is a wide area near the mouth of the river where the sea (salt) water mixes with fresh water, forming brackish water.

- The **mouth** is the point where the river reaches the sea.

- At this point, the river drops much of the load it has been carrying, which sometimes forms a **delta**.

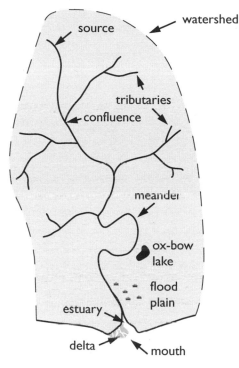

Fig. 2.3.1: River basin

2.4 River processes

Three processes occur as a river flows from its source to its mouth. These are erosion, transportation and deposition. There are four types of erosion and four types of transportation.

Erosion

As the river moves through the river basin, it alters the landscape due to the wearing away and removal of land caused by the following processes:

- **Attrition** occurs when particles of load collide and knock pieces off each other.

- **Abrasion** occurs when smaller material rubs against the bed and banks of the river.

- **Corrosion** occurs when acid in the water dissolves particles of rocks from the bed and banks of the river.

- **Hydraulic action** is the sheer force of the water and air forcing itself into the soil and moving away parts of the bed and banks of the river.

Transportation

Once the material (known as **load**) has been eroded, it is then carried along the river by the following processes:

- **Traction** is the rolling of stones along the river bed.
- **Saltation** is the movement of particles 'leap-frogging' along the river bed.
- **Suspension** is the movement of material that is carried within the water flow.
- **Solution** is the movement of material that is dissolved in the water.

(Sometimes the process of carrying material on top of the water, e.g. twigs, is called **flotation**.)

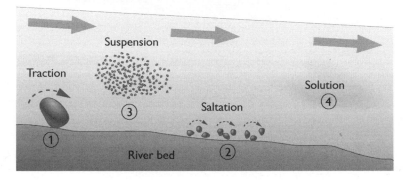

Deposition

When the river slows down, the load is 'dumped'. This is known as deposition. Large boulders are deposited first and fine sediment last.

2.5 Features of the upper course

V-shaped valleys and waterfalls are the main features of the upper course of a river.

V-shaped valley

This is a feature of erosion. It occurs when the river erodes downwards into the land by abrasion and hydraulic action. This is called vertical erosion. The valley sides are then shaped by the weather, plants and animals (weathering).

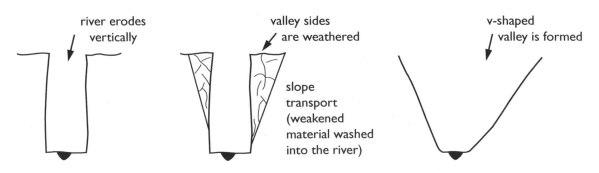

Fig. 2.5.1: V-shaped valley formation

Waterfall

This is a feature of erosion. It occurs when a river flowing over hard rock meets a band of softer, less resistant rock.

- Hydraulic action and abrasion erode the softer rock forming a 'step' in the river bed.

- The softer rock is undercut and the hard rock is left as an overhang. A plunge pool is formed at the base of the waterfall; this plunge pool is deepened by hydraulic action, corrosion and abrasion as the pebbles erode its base.

- The overhang eventually collapses and in this way the waterfall retreats towards the source of the river.

- As the erosion continues, a gorge is formed.

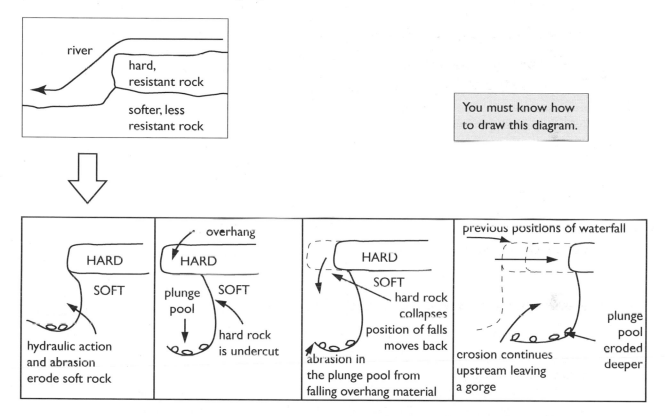

You must know how to draw this diagram.

Fig. 2.5.2: Waterfall formation

2.6 Features of the lower course

Meanders, ox-bow lakes, deltas and flood plains are the main features of the lower course of a river.

Meanders

This is a feature of erosion and deposition. The river is dynamic – it is constantly changing its shape and therefore has a lot of meanders (bends) in it. These meanders are formed by **lateral** (sideways) **erosion**.

(A) : **Outside of a meander**

river cliff

fast velocity

erosion (hydraulic action and abrasion)

deeper water

(B) : **Inside of a meander**

river beach / slip-off slope

slow velocity

deposition

shallow water

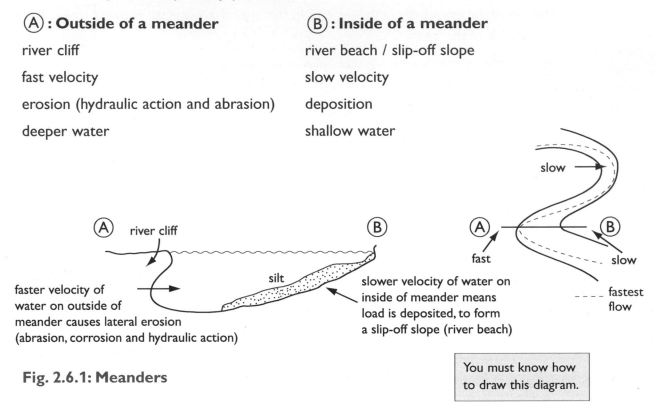

Fig. 2.6.1: Meanders

> You must know how to draw this diagram.

Ox-bow lake

This is a feature of erosion and deposition. It occurs where the horseshoe-shaped meander becomes tighter, until the ends become very close together and join to form a separate lake.

(1) The outsides of two meanders are eroded by **hydraulic action** and **abrasion**.

(2) The river becomes more **sinuous** (has more curves and turns). This results in a narrow neck of land remaining between the two river cliffs.

(3) Eventually, perhaps during a flood, the narrow neck of land is eroded away and the water takes the more direct straight route downstream.

(4) **Deposition** occurs and eventually the old meander loop is separated from the river and forms an ox-bow lake.

Evaporation will usually cause the lake to become dry eventually.

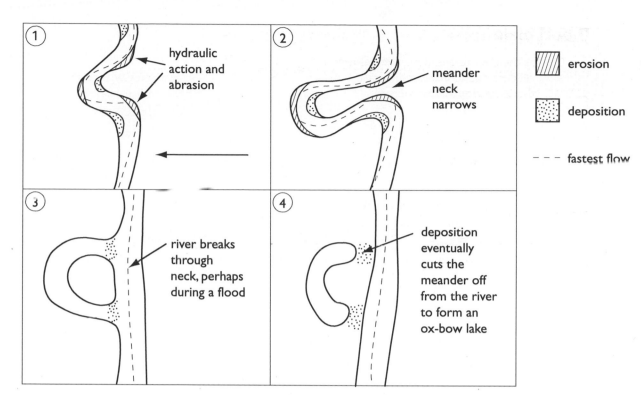

Fig. 2.6.2: Ox-bow lake formation

Deltas

This is a feature of deposition. Examples are the Nile Delta and the Mississippi Delta.

- As large rivers approach the sea, they carry a large amount of **load** (material) in suspension.

- The speed (velocity) of the river is reduced as it reaches the more powerful sea, so it has less energy and deposits its load to form new land.

- The coarser material is deposited first (in topset beds), the medium sized silt (in foreset beds) and then the finer material (in bottomset beds).

- With time, more and more sand and silt is deposited.

- The river divides into channels called **distributaries** which flow round the deposits of new land.

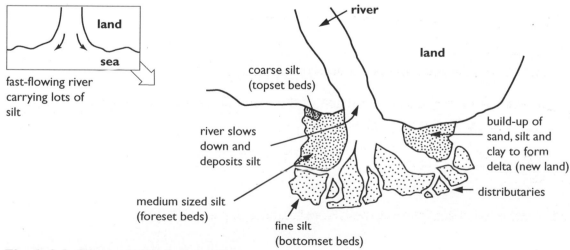

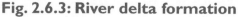

Fig. 2.6.3: River delta formation

Flood plain

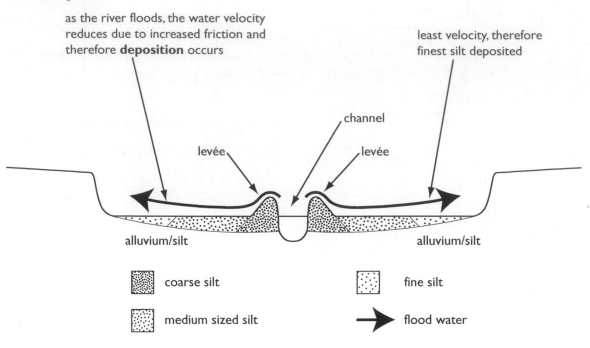

as the river floods, the water velocity reduces due to increased friction and therefore **deposition** occurs

least velocity, therefore finest silt deposited

channel

levée

levée

alluvium/silt

alluvium/silt

coarse silt

fine silt

medium sized silt

flood water

Fig. 2.6.4: Flood plain

This is a feature of **deposition**. It occurs when a river floods and deposits its load.

- As the water spills out of its channel, friction increases, the water velocity decreases and deposition occurs.

- The larger pieces of load are deposited first, often forming natural **levees** near the channel.

- Finer sediment is transported further away from the channel.

- The flat land onto which flood water flows is known as the flood plain.

Sample questions

Try these sample questions. Suggested answers are given at the back of the book.

Q. 2.1 Hydraulic action is one type of river erosion.
    (a) Name another river erosion process. (1)
    (b) Describe how this process works. (3)

2.2 What do you call the material transported in a river? (1)

2.3 How does the size and shape of the material transported in a river change from source to mouth? (3)

2.7 Coastal erosion

There are four types of coastal erosion.

- **Hydraulic action** is the force of the waves against the cliffs. The water traps air in cracks and caves. The air is compressed, forcing the rock to weaken and eventually break.

- **Corrosion** is caused by the acid in the seawater spray dissolving the rock.

- **Attrition** is caused by pebbles hitting each other in the waves. This makes the pebbles smaller and rounder and eventually they become sand.

- **Abrasion** is the effect of waves throwing pebbles at the cliffs. This erodes the cliffs at their base.

The features of erosion are:

- headlands and bays

- caves, arches, stacks and stumps.

Headlands and bays

These are features of erosion and deposition.

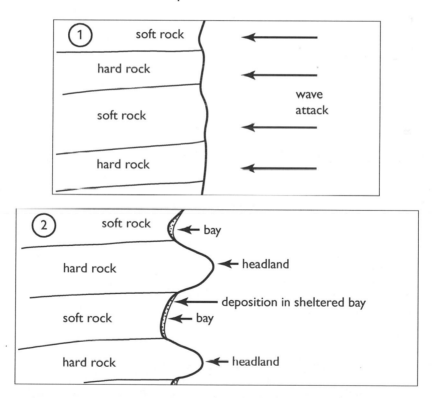

Fig. 2.7.1: Headland and bay formation on discordant coastline

(1) Waves attack a discordant coastline of alternating hard and soft rock. The soft rock erodes at a faster rate than the hard rock.

(2) Headlands are created from the hard rock and bays are eroded from the soft rock between them. Deposition also occurs in sheltered bays.

Caves, arches, stacks and stumps

These are features of erosion. See Fig. 2.7.2 opposite.

(1) Waves attack a fault in the rock by hydraulic action and abrasion.

(2) The fault is enlarged to form a cave. A blowhole may appear on the headland due to upward erosion by waves on the roof of the cave.

(3) Hydraulic action and abrasion widen and deepen the cave and eventually cut through the headland to form an arch.

(4) Undercutting, weathering and lack of support for the arch lead to collapse, leaving a stack.

(5) Weathering and erosion turns the stack into a stump.

As the cliff retreats through erosion by waves, a platform of rock extending into the sea may be left. This is called a wave cut platform.

Sample question

Try this sample question. The answer is given at the back of the book.

Q. 2.4 Describe the processes involved in the erosion of a headland.   (5)

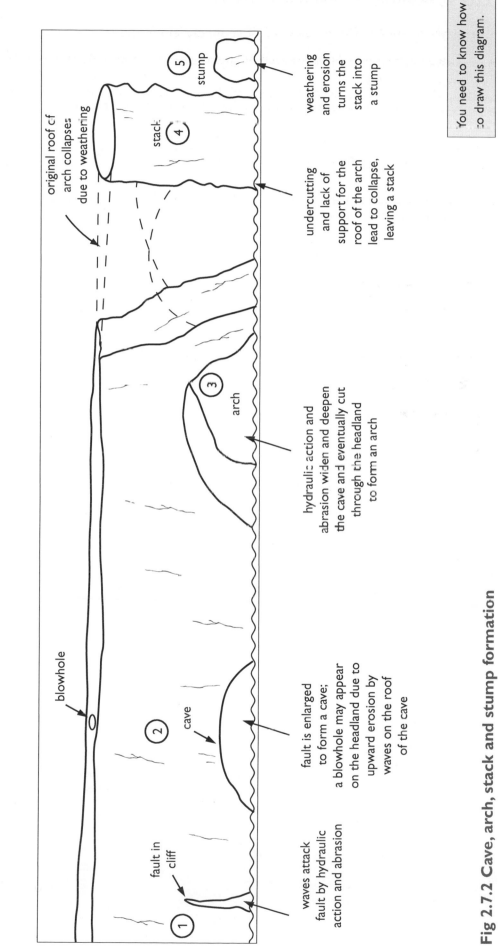

You need to know how to draw this diagram.

Fig 2.7.2 Cave, arch, stack and stump formation

25

2.8 Coastal transportation

Longshore drift is the movement of sediment along the beach by waves.

- The swash moves up the beach at the angle determined by the direction of the prevailing wind.

- After the wave has broken, the backwash returns to the sea at a 90° angle.

- In this way, sand and pebbles are moved along the beach.

- The sand and pebbles will build up against a groyne.

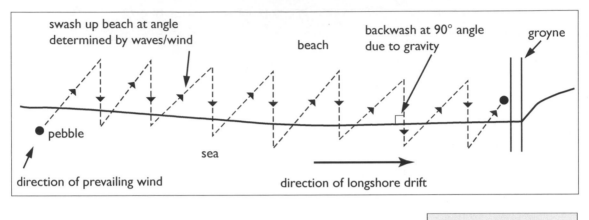

Fig 2.8.1: Coastal transportation

You need to know how to draw this diagram.

2.9 Coastal deposition

Spits are features of coastal deposition. An example is Hurst Castle Spit in Hampshire.

You need to know how to draw this diagram.

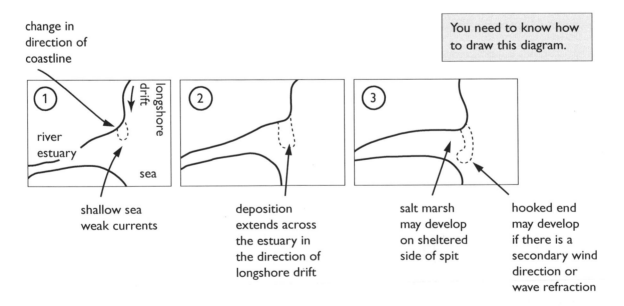

Fig 2.9.1 Beach and spit formation

1. A spit is created when longshore drift transports pebbles and sand towards a corner in a coastline. At the point where there is a change in the direction of the coastline and shallow water with weak currents, the pebbles and sand are deposited.

2. Over time the deposition will extend into the sea in the direction of the longshore drift.

3. A salt marsh will then develop on the sheltered side of the spit. The spit may develop a hooked end if there is a secondary wind direction or wave refraction.

Sample question

Try this sample question. The answer is given at the back of the book.

Q. 2.5 Describe and draw the processes involved in the formation of a spit.   (5)

2.10 Landslides

(Although this section is not required for the CE syllabus it is useful in order to give context to coastal erosion. However, the term mass movement can be used to describe the movement of weathered soil and rock on a slope, and it is necessary for you to know this term.)

A landslide occurs when the rock and/or soil that make up a slope give way. The causes of a landslide may include:

- the angle of the slope
- gravity
- the structure of the rock
- saturated soil or rock
- undercutting at the base of the rock by waves or mining
- building on the slope
- deforestation
- tectonic activity.

2.11 Causes of flooding – river and coastal

The causes of flooding can be broken down into: climatic, physical and human.

Climatic reasons
- Heavy rainfall over a short or long period of time.
- Ground that is saturated as a result of previous rainfall.
- Melting snow and glaciers.
- Hurricanes causing wave surges.

Physical reasons

- Narrow steep-sided valleys cause surface run-off to reach rivers rapidly after a storm.
- A small river basin causing rapid surface run-off.
- Impermeable rock causing rapid surface run-off.
- Low-lying coastal areas.

Human reasons

- Urbanisation can lead to an increase in tarmac and drains, which cause rapid surface run-off.
- Deforestation in a river basin, which leads to less water being taken up by roots.
- The diversion of a river or the narrowing of a channel.
- Deforestation and the loss of tree roots mean that the soil is loosened and when rain falls and travels as surface run-off, it takes with it soil that washes into the river and silts up the river, displacing water.

2.12 Effects of floods

The effects of flooding can include the following:

- Buildings being washed away or damaged.
- People and animals being drowned.
- Communications damaged due to closed roads and impassable railways.
- Crops being ruined (and the agricultural economy suffering).
- Insurance claims.
- Drinking water being contaminated by sewage, leading to disease.

A beneficial effect is that silt that is deposited by flooding rivers provides fertile soil for farming.

2.13 Flood control and prevention

Various things can be done to prevent and control flooding.

- The construction of dams to control the amount of water being discharged.
- The construction of levees and dykes to contain water.
- The straightening of meanders to enable flood water to escape more quickly.
- Afforestation to increase transpiration and infiltration (water will be removed from the river basin as it is taken up by the roots).
- Sandbagging to prevent the flooding of buildings.
- Construction of sea defences.

Case study 2.1 – Boscastle floods, 2004

Flash floods occurred in the valleys of the River Valency and the River Jordan on 16th August 2004.

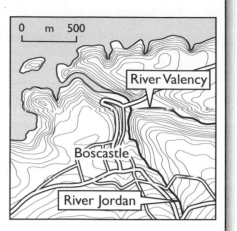

Causes

Physical

The village of Boscastle is situated:

- in a narrow valley with interlocking spurs which acted like a funnel

- in a steep valley which encouraged rapid run-off

- on a flat flood plain

- in an area where the soil is impermeable clay which does not allow much infiltration.

Climatic

- 185 mm of rain fell in five hours.

- The soil was saturated from recent rainfall so no more rain could infiltrate.

- The collision of winds on a very warm day caused the excessive rainfall. (The air mass from the south met the air mass from the south-west and converged on Bodmin which led to towering cumulonimbus clouds. The air was very unstable and the clouds were up to 10 km high.)

Human

- The natural channel of the river had been walled (for the construction of the B3263 and a pedestrian area) which prevented it from adjusting to a variation in the discharge of water.

- The village had been built on a flat flood plain.

- There was no flood control system.

- Cars, trees and boulders became stuck under the bridge which caused a temporary dam causing the water to build up behind it.

- The sewers and drainage systems were old and small in capacity; they broke and the water that was in them took an overland route.

Effects

- Fifty cars were swept into the harbour.

- The bridge was washed away and roads were submerged under 2.75 m of water, making communication difficult.

- The sewerage system burst.

Effects (continued)

- For health and safety reasons Boscastle was declared inaccessible.
- The Museum of Witchcraft lost 50% of its artefacts.
- Four buildings were demolished and 58 flooded and the High Street was badly damaged.
- The visitors' centre, a clothes shop and two gift shops were badly damaged.
- The youth hostel was flooded.
- People were in shock and there was concern about hypothermia or being swept away.
- There was no power in the village for some time. (An emergency generator had to be flown in.)
- 90% of the economy in Boscastle is based on tourism and there were still three weeks of the summer holidays left; twenty accommodation providers were shut.
- Visitors whose cars had been washed away were not able to leave.

Responses

- A speedy, well-coordinated and well-resourced rescue operation ensured that remarkably there was no loss of life. Even by the standards of more economically developed countries (MEDCs), this was outstanding and a tribute to Britain's rescue services.
- Emergency workers rescued residents and holiday-makers from a 32 km stretch of the north Cornwall coast.
- Hundreds were evacuated from homes, rooftops (120 from rooftops), trees and vehicles.
- Seven helicopters from the Coastguards, Royal Navy and RAF were used.
- People took emergency shelter in The Rectory, which is on high ground.
- The village was cordoned off by the building inspectors for the clean-up operation.
- People dug out guttering and removed rubble so that the water could flow away.
- Sandbagging was used as a form of defence.
- People came to see the catastrophe, despite the 'no entry' signs.
- Prince Charles and the Deputy Prime Minister at the time, John Prescott, came to see the damage.
- There was a church service to give thanks that no one had died.
- The repairs were very costly and time consuming.
- There was a huge fund-raising effort to help rebuild the village.
- Insurance is now costlier in Boscastle.

Flood control and prevention

- The Environment Agency carried out a major investigation.

- A £2 million grant was given to Boscastle to help with flood prevention.

- No more schools or old people's homes are to be built in the valley.

- The Environment Agency removed debris from upstream, which meant more room for the water to flow freely under the new bridge.

- A flood defence system (building a flood wall, widening the River Jordan, raising car parks, removing bridges and using relief channels) was planned and is now almost complete. Also included building a high-arched single-span bridge which would not impede flood water and debris.

Case Study 2.2 – Flooding in Bangladesh, 2004

Floods occur each year in Bangladesh. The majority of Bangladesh's 140 million inhabitants live on the floodplains of the Ganges and Brahmaputra and they need the floods to enable them to grow rice and jute. The floods also deposit silt which makes the soil fertile. However, the inundation (flooding) is often so intense that lives and crops are ruined. Bangladesh suffers from two types of flood: river flooding and storm surges (coastal flooding) from the Bay of Bengal.

Bangladesh can get more rain in four months than London gets in two years!

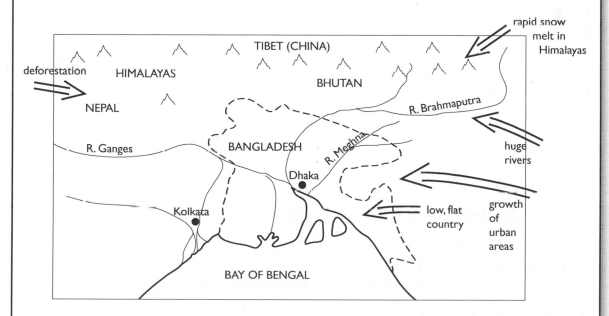

Fig.2.13.1: Location and causes of the flood in Bangladesh

Causes

Climatic

- Bangladesh has a monsoon climate, receiving between 1800 mm and 2600 mm of rainfall per year. However, 80% of this rainfall takes place in four months (June to September).

- There are high temperatures from June to September, causing ice and snow to melt in the Himalayas where the Ganges and Brahmaputra have their sources and tributaries.

- Tropical cyclones which are funnelled up the Bay of Bengal make sea levels rise and stop the river flood water escaping. As the land becomes shallower, the water builds up to form a surge up to 6 metres in height.

Physical

- Half the country lies less than 6 metres above sea level.

- Most of the population live on the silt deposited by the Ganges and Brahmaputra Rivers, which forms a delta. However, the continuous deposition of silt tends to block the main channels and raise the height of river beds, making severe floods more likely.

- Once rivers overflow their banks, the water can spread a vast distance across the flat delta floodplain.

- High tides in the Bay of Bengal stop the flood water from being able to escape.

Human

- Global warming is causing glaciers in the Himalayas to melt and the sea level of the Bay of Bengal to rise.

- Urbanisation on the delta floodplain has led to more run-off and a shorter lag time (the time between maximum rainfall and maximum discharge in the river).

- Deforestation in the upper course of the river (Nepal) has led to more run-off which allows more sediment to build up, which leads to a higher risk of flooding.

Effects

Environmental

- The flood was so deep in places that only the tops of roofs and trees could be seen.

- Large areas of the capital city of Dhaka were flooded, particularly the eastern area. The western area was protected by an embankment.

- 'Char' areas (low flat land made up of deposited silt) were destroyed.

- The deposits left by this severe flood were infertile sand rather than silt. When the water receded the land was infertile.

Social

- Thousands of hectares of crops were damaged or destroyed, which led to food shortages.

- At least 1,679 people were killed. In an LEDC (less economically developed country) many are too poor to own a telephone or TV and did not get advance warning to escape.

- Two thirds of the country was flooded.

- 20 600 livestock died, leading to food shortages.

- Infrastructure such as roads, railways and bridges were destroyed. Thousands of kilometres of roads were closed.

- Three million homes were destroyed or damaged and two million people were made homeless.

- Most parts of the country were without electricity for several weeks.

- Flood water had polluted wells so there was no safe drinking water.

- As people evacuated to higher ground, crowding aided the spread of dysentery, cholera and diarrhoea.

- Hospitals were full.

- 23 000 schools were damaged.

- People ran out of money to buy food and could not work as the land was submerged.

- Dhaka International Airport was submerged in water.

Responses

- Food grain was imported.

- Medical care and water purification tablets were provided in treatment centres and by mobile teams. This was easier in Dhaka. In rural areas distribution was by boat.

- Newspapers gave advice on how to avoid drinking dirty water.

- The poorest were identified by Save the Children Fund and Oxfam and given food assistance.

- People took out loans during or after the flood from Mohajons (money lenders who charge very high interest rates e.g. 200% per year). Some sold any remaining possessions.

- After the bad flooding that occurred in 1988, the Flood Action Plan (costing over $650 million) was proposed by rich countries to be funded by the World Bank. The plan included the construction of large embankments to protect major cities, roads, rail and agricultural land.

- There has been some criticism of this plan, as to whether it is sustainable, as it narrows the flood plain and increases the height of the rivers, depriving many areas of fish and fertile silt. It would also be very expensive.

- Appropriate technology has been suggested as an alternative. This would allow flooding but hopefully control extreme flooding. The Appropriate Technology Plan would also include improving early warning systems, by the distribution of leaflets and enlisting 33 000 volunteers to educate people on preparing and coping with future floods.

- As part of the Flood Action Plan, flood shelters (made of concrete and built on stilts) have also been constructed in low lying agricultural areas. Other plans include: the building of dams to control the water; improved flood warning systems; giving after-care such as food, drinking water, tents and medicine, as well as help provided to plant the next year's crops.

- The 1998 flood killed more people than the 2004 flood. Therefore forecasting, earlier deliveries of aid and the Flood Action Plan have had some effect.

Case study 2.3 – Hurricane Katrina (coastal flooding), 2005

Hurricane Katrina hit the Florida coast on 25th August 2005. She veered inland towards Louisiana making landfall at Grand Isle (90 km south of New Orleans). She then hit New Orleans, Biloxi, Mobile and Jackson. Katrina was a Force 5 hurricane on the Saffir-Simpson scale (which means the wind speeds were faster than 249 km/h). A storm surge (wave) built under the hurricane and flooded the area when the hurricane reached land.

Causes

Climatic

- The hurricane formed when a cluster of thunderstorms drifted over the warm Caribbean Sea.

- The warm air from the ocean and the storm combined and rose – this created low pressure.

- Trade winds blowing in opposing directions and the Coriolis force caused the storm to spin.

- The rising warm air caused pressure to decrease at higher altitudes.

- The air rose faster and faster to fill this low pressure, drawing more warm air off the sea and sucking cooler, drier air downwards.

- The storm moved over the ocean and picked up more warm, moist air. Wind speeds started to pick up as more air was sucked into the low-pressure centre.

- There was an eye of calm winds surrounded by a spinning vortex of high winds and heavy rain.

- A large dome of water was created under the hurricane, which turned into a storm surge when it hit land.

Human

- New Orleans is built in a bowl – the Mississippi had been controlled with levees and dams for years, and New Orleans was only in existence because of these.

- The city was suffering from subsidence as groundwater was extracted from underground and the coastline was disappearing. Louisiana has the highest rate of erosion in North America.

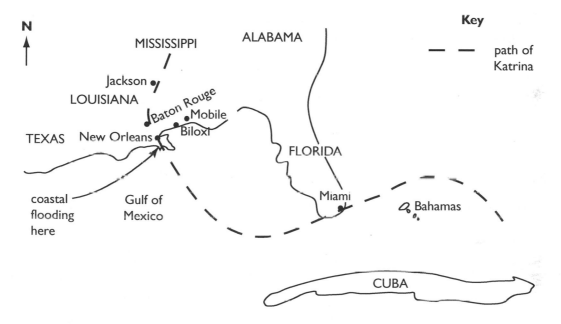

Fig. 2.13.2: Path of Hurricane Katrina

Effects

Environmental

- A surge of 9 metres in Biloxi covered the land with water.

- Protective coastal mangroves were destroyed.

- The poorly maintained levees on the Mississippi broke, inundating New Orleans with flood water (80% of the city was inundated).

- Flood water and fires destroyed many buildings.

- Trees and vegetation were destroyed by the flood.

- Fresh water was contaminated with salt water.

Social

- 1300 people were killed, mainly in New Orleans.

- There were 500 000 refugees.

- The flood water was polluted with oil and infested with snakes.

- Those who could not evacuate were left with a lack of water, food, power and fuel. They could not recharge their mobile phones and therefore could not use them to communicate.

- The disaster revealed the poverty of New Orleans, e.g. 50% of children were on welfare. Afro-American leaders became angry that this section of society was left behind.

- Poverty resulted in looting for food and the army's violent response came more quickly than aid.

- Many took refuge in the Superdome despite the fact that there was no proper sanitation or proper supplies; it became crowded and overheated.

Economic

- Work at oil refineries and platforms was halted.

- Casinos and businesses were looted.

- 400 000 homes and businesses were without power in Alabama.

- Huge blasts from a chemical plant rocked the city on 2nd September.

- Many left their businesses and have not returned, as they have been forced to start a new life elsewhere.

Responses

- 'Katrina was a national failure.' (Congressional Report, February 2006)

- Aid was delayed by five days – the Director of Federal Emergency Management Agency (FEMA), Michael Brown, was dismissed from his post a week after the hurricane.

- The evacuation drill consisted of saying 'leave town'. Many could not speak English, could not afford to leave or were too ill to leave. Disaster drills did not consider the levee break.

- President Bush had poor and incomplete advice, and a late decision to carry out a compulsory evacuation led to deaths and prolonged suffering.

- There was no warning and no buses were provided for evacuation.

- Helicopters dropped sandbags into the breach in the 17th Street Canal and earthmovers built a causeway allowing trucks to bring stones to repair levees.

- A temporary steel barrier was built at the mouth of the canal to seal it from Lake Pontchartrain.

- Areas were then pumped free of water.

- The Red Cross served 995 000 meals in one day alone.

- The congressional committee spent months planning how to rebuild and revitalise housing, business and transport, and how levees and flood defences could be improved to prevent large-scale flooding in the future.

- Bush promised $3.1 billion towards repairs and improvements.

- The US Army Corps planned temporary repairs in time for the next hurricane season.

- The Mississippi River Gulf Outlet, built in the 1960s, allowed ships easy access to the Gulf of Mexico via the Port of New Orleans. However, the channel increased from 91 m to 914 m wide due to deliberate widening and natural action. The storm surge of Katrina passed up this channel. The channel was closed in 2009.

Other facts

- FEMA suffered from a lack of trained and experienced personnel.

- Computer models predicted the levee failure, so the authorities should have been prepared.

- The impact of global warming causing sea levels to rise will make flooding an even greater threat in the future.

- Some believe that the chaos of Katrina has exposed deep divisions in New Orleans and US society. (Congressman Elijah Cummings said, 'We cannot allow it to be said by history that the difference between those who lived and ... died ... was nothing more than poverty, age or skin colour.')

Summary

You should now know the following:

1. The different types of weathering.

2. The different rock types.

3. The features of a river basin.

4. The different river processes.

5. The features of the upper and lower courses of a river.

6. The features and causes of coastal erosion.

7. The main features of coastal transportation and deposition.

8. The main causes of landslides.

9. The causes and effects of and human response to a specific flood.

Test yourself

Before moving on to the next chapter, make sure you can answer the following questions. The answers to questions 1–6 are at the back of the book.

1. Using the words given below, write out the following paragraph, filling in the gaps.

   transports   outside   speed   inside   reduces

   river   cliff   increases   river beach   slip-off slope   delta

   Velocity is the . . . . of the water. Deposition is the 'dumping' of a load when the river's velocity . . . . Load is the material which the river . . . . Load can be deposited by rivers at their mouth; the feature formed is called a . . . . It is also deposited on the . . . . bend of a meander; the feature formed is called a . . . .

2. Copy and complete the table to show how the shape and size of a river's load changes from upper course to lower course.

	Upper course	**Lower course**
Size of load		
Shape of load		
Main methods of transportation		

3. To which type of weathering will the following be most prone?
   (a) Rocks in a tropical rain forest.
   (b) Mountainous areas.
   (c) Rocks in a desert.

4. Match the definition to the term and write them down. (The first one is done for you.) Note: you will have come across some of these terms in Chapter 1.

   River basin – an area of land drained by a river and its tributaries

River basin	the movement of water over the surface of the land back to the sea
Watershed	rocks that allow water to pass through
Source	when the river's load collides and breaks into smaller pieces
Mouth	the downwards movement of water through tiny pores in the soil
Permeable	the movement of water through the soil back to the sea
Impermeable	the loss of moisture to the air from plants
Evaporation	the amount of water that passes a given point at a given time, measured in cumecs (cubic metres per second)
Transpiration	an area of land drained by a river and its tributaries
Through flow	the start of a river
Ground water storage	where a river meets the sea
Infiltration	water stored in rocks below the ground
Surface run-off	the material that a river carries
River discharge	a type of erosion caused by the force of the water breaking particles of rock from the river bank
Load	rocks that do not allow water to pass through
Attrition	the loss of water to the air when the water has turned into water vapour
Corrosion	a type of erosion caused by the acids in the river dissolving the rocks
Hydraulic action	the boundary of the river basin, usually marked by a ridge of high land

5. (a) Which of the following is a process that involves waves hitting cliffs and eroding them?
        ● hydraulic action
        ● deposition
        ● longshore drift
        ● saltation

    (b) Longshore drift can create a:
        ● waterfall
        ● stack
        ● stump
        ● spit

    (c) A stump is an eroded:
        ● cave
        ● stack
        ● spit
        ● meander

6. Draw a diagram to explain the process of longshore drift.

7. (a) For an area you have studied, explain why there was a flood.
    (b) Describe the effects of the flood.
    (c) How can floods be controlled?

8. Write the definitions of these words and phrases and then ask someone to check them.

Words you need to know	Words that will be useful
bay	abrasion
beach	arch
bedding plane	attrition
dam	biological weathering
erosion	cave
fault	chemical weathering
fetch	confluence
flood plain	corrosion
gorge	delta
headland	deposition
hydo-electric power	river basin
joint	dyke
levee	estuary
longshore drift	freeze-thaw weathering
mass movement	hydraulic action
meander	igneous rock
permeable	impermeable

Words you need to know	Words that will be useful
plunge pool	interlocking spurs
porous	landslide
reservoir	limestone
river basin	load
river cliff	metamorphic rock
run-off	mouth
scree	onion-skin weathering (exfoliation)
sedimentary rock	ox-bow lake
slip-off slope (river beach)	physical weathering
source	quarry
spit	saltation
stack	solution
transportation	stump
tributary	suspension
waterfall	thalweg
watertable	traction
weathering	v-shaped valley
	watershed

Chapter 3: Earthquakes and volcanoes

3.1 Tectonic plates and plate boundaries

Tectonic plates are the huge slabs of rock that form the Earth's crust and that float on the mantle (the semi-solid rock beneath the crust).

- The lightest and thickest plates are called **continental plates** and form land.
- The thinner but heavier plates are called **oceanic plates** and have sea over them.

The movement of plates is called **continental drift**. This can push the plates together or push them apart. Continental drift occurs due to the movement of the magma in the mantle below the plates. The movement of the magma is caused by convection currents generated by the immense heat at the Earth's core.

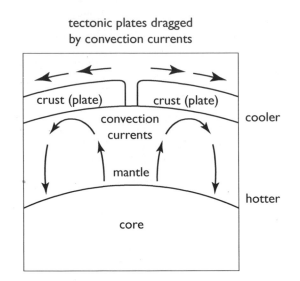

Fig. 3.1.1: Continental drift and plate movement

The edges where the plates meet are called **plate boundaries**. There are four types of plate boundary: constructive, destructive, conservative (or sliding) and collision.

Constructive plate boundary

- At a constructive plate boundary two plates move apart.
- Magma rises to the surface, due to gas bubbles in the magma that make it lighter than the surrounding rock.
- Volcanoes are formed.
- Gentle eruptions occur which may continue for years.

Most constructive boundaries are under the sea and form chains of volcanic islands. The Mid-Atlantic Ridge is the most famous.

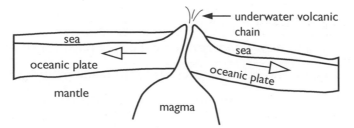

Fig. 3.1.2: Constructive plate boundary

Destructive plate boundary

- At a destructive plate boundary, an oceanic and a continental plate collide.

- The heavier oceanic plate sinks under the continental plate into what is known as a subduction zone.

- The melted crust rises (due to the gas bubbles in the magma that make it lighter than the surrounding rock) to form explosive, dangerous volcanoes.

- When the two plates rub together, friction occurs, leading to earthquakes.

The most famous destructive boundary is the Pacific Ring of Fire, which forms a band of earthquakes and volcanoes round the edge of the Pacific Ocean. A destructive plate boundary was also the cause of the Soufrière Hills volcano, Montserrat.

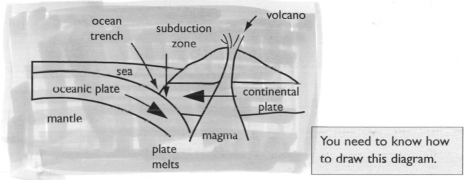

You need to know how to draw this diagram.

Fig. 3.1.3: Destructive plate boundary

Conservative (or sliding) plate boundary

- At a conservative plate boundary, two plates slide past each other.

- The plates become locked and tension builds up over years.

- Eventually the plates will jolt past each other, causing powerful earthquakes.

- Volcanic activity does not occur.

The most famous of these is the San Andreas fault.

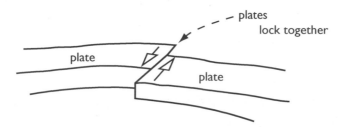

Fig. 3.1.4: Conservative plate boundary

Collision plate boundary

- At a collision plate boundary, two continental plates push together.

- Neither sinks beneath the other as they are both made from light rock.

- The plates buckle to form fold mountains and violent earthquakes occur.

- Volcanic activity does not occur.

- The area where the earthquake starts underground is known as the focus. Directly above the focus, on the Earth's surface, is the epicentre.

The Himalayas are the most famous fold mountains.

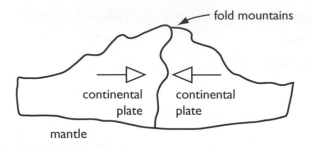

Fig. 3.1.5: Collision plate boundary

3.2 Types of volcano

There are two types of volcano: composite and shield.

Composite volcanoes

- These occur in areas of destructive plate boundaries.

- The eruptions are violent, ejecting thick and sticky lava.

- Ash and lava are ejected into the air and descend as slow-flowing, thick lava. The process is then repeated, building up layers of ash and lava.

- Pyroclastic flows (hot gas and ash) travelling more than 100 mph can flatten and burn everything in their path.

- Lahars (melted ice or rain mixed with ash) can occur.

- Thick layers of ash leave areas uninhabitable.

Examples of composite volcanoes are the Soufrière Hills, Montserrat and Mount Etna.

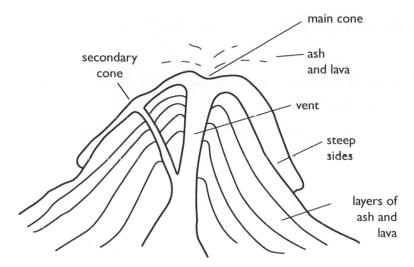

Fig. 3.2.1: Composite volcano

Shield volcanoes

- These occur in areas of constructive plate boundaries.

- Wide, gently-sloping volcanoes eject thin, runny lava.

- The eruptions are not explosive and are less likely to result in loss of life.

Examples of shield volcanoes are Iceland and Hawaii.

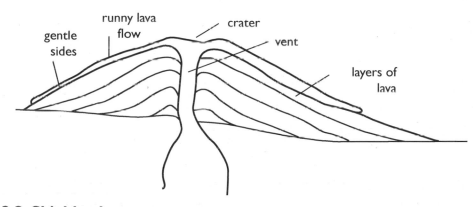

Fig. 3.2.2: Shield volcano

3.3 Immediate effects of a volcanic eruption

- Ash fall.

- Mud flow (lahar) – ash mixed with rain or melted ice.

- Pyroclastic flow – hot gas and ash rolling down cone.

- Lava flow – molten rock.

- Pyroclastic bombs (volcanic bombs) – lava cooling when ejected into air, falling as solid rock.

3.4 Preparing for and reacting to a volcanic eruption

- Hazard maps can be drawn (as in Montserrat) to show which areas are safest and which are most at risk.

- Lava flows can be diverted by channels or explosives, dammed or sprayed with cool water.

- People can be evacuated.

- Seismometers can record the earthquakes that occur as the magma rises.

- Tiltmeters can record changes in the shape of a volcano before an eruption.

- Satellites can record changes in the temperature and shape of a volcano before an eruption.

3.5 Why people live near volcanoes

Despite the dangers of living near a volcano, people continue to live in these areas for a number of reasons:

- Interest in volcanoes generates tourism and therefore boosts the local economy.

- Geothermal energy can be produced from the rising steam, e.g. in Iceland and New Zealand.

- Fertile soil is produced by the weathering of volcanic ash. This soil is particularly good for grapevines.

- Minerals, such as gold and diamonds, can be found in the area.

3.6 Factors determining the severity of damage

A number of factors determine the severity of damage caused by a volcano:

- The type of plate boundary that has caused the volcano. Destructive plate boundaries cause violent volcanoes.

- The volcano's proximity to a large settlement. Those situated near large cities where population is dense cause more deaths than those in less populated areas.

- The wealth of the country in which it erupts. An MEDC can afford scientific prediction instruments, a quick reaction force and good medical care for the injured.

Case study 3.1 – Soufrière Hills volcano, Montserrat (LEDC), 1995

Facts

- After a long period of dormancy the Soufrière Hills volcano became active in 1995 and eruptions have continued to the present day.

Cause

- The Soufrière Hills volcano is located on a destructive plate boundary of three plates: South American, North American and Caribbean.

Fig. 3.6.1: Location of Soufrière Hills volcano

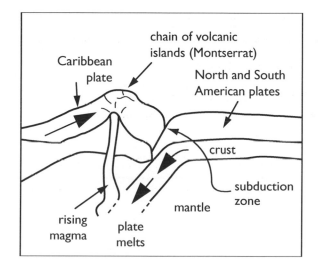

Fig. 3.6.2: Destructive plate boundary (North and South American and Caribbean plates)

Effects

Environmental

- Pyroclastic flow burned vegetation.

- Ash covered two thirds of the island.

- Wildlife disappeared.

- Coral reef and sea creatures died from the ash washed into the sea.

- New land was formed when the pyroclastic flow solidified in the sea.

Economic

- The agricultural economy was ruined.

- The tourist economy was ruined – the airport was closed for ten years.

Social

- Montserrat is a UK dependency therefore the UK is obliged to offer aid.

- 60% of housing was destroyed.

- 23 people died in the pyroclastic flow of 25th June 1997.

- 8000 inhabitants left Montserrat for the UK and Antigua.

- Hospitals were destroyed.

- Few schools were left intact.

- There was a lack of clean water and sewerage facilities.

Human response

- The Montserrat volcano observatory was built to monitor the volcano with seismometers and tiltmeters.

- A hazard map was drawn up to highlight danger and safe zones.

- International aid was received from the UK and other countries.

- Inhabitants were evacuated to the UK and Antigua.

- There was a concert in the Royal Albert Hall to raise money. This money allowed the UK to send out *HMS Liverpool* with emergency showers and kitchen facilities for the islanders.

Case study 3.2 – Mount Etna volcano, Sicily (MEDC), 2001

Facts

- Mount Etna erupted on 12th July 2001.

Cause

- Mount Etna is located on a destructive plate boundary where the African plate subducts under the Eurasian plate.

Effects

Environmental

- The lava flows reached temperatures of 1000 °C.

Economic

- Lava flows destroyed several ski lift pylons, a tourist car park, and a barn containing snow ploughs.

- Less snow settled on the sides of the volcano due to the heat of the lava, affecting the winter ski season later that year.

- The airport in Catania was forced to close while the runways are cleared of ash.

- The agricultural and tourist economies of the towns on Etna's slopes were affected.

Human response

- Dams of earth and volcanic rock were put up to protect the tourist base of Rifugio Sapienza. These diverted the flow and kept it under control.

- The Army brought in heavy earth-moving equipment to block and divert lava flows.

- Religious ceremonies were held by local residents in Nicolosi, a village perched on the side of the volcano, to try to reduce the impact of the eruption.

- The Italian government promised to reduce taxes for villagers to help them get through the crisis, and handed out more than £5.6m in aid.

Case study 3.3 – Eyjafjallajökull volcano, Iceland (MEDC), 2010

Facts

- The volcano is located under the Eyjafjallajoekull glacier in the southern part of Iceland.

- The Eyjafjallajökull volcano began erupting in March 2010. There was an explosive phase from 14th April to 21st April, followed by a drop in intensity and then increased activity at the start of May.

- As the lava came out of the volcano it cooled very quickly as the glacier was on top. This caused the lava to shatter into tiny fragments of ash.

- The glacier melt water poured into the vent, which created steam and caused the mineral ash to reach heights of 6–10 km.

Cause

- Iceland is situated on the Mid Atlantic Ridge, a constructive plate boundary running through the middle of the Atlantic Ocean.

- The Eurasian Plate is moving very slowly eastwards and the North American Plate is moving very slowly westwards. The two plates are diverging.

- The Eyjafjallajökull glacier lies on top of the volcano.

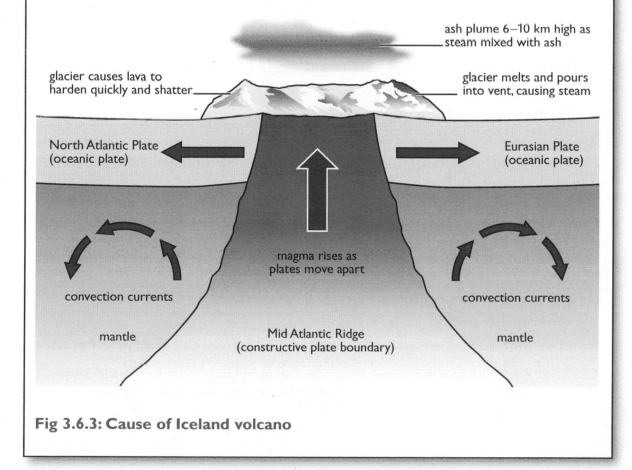

Fig 3.6.3: Cause of Iceland volcano

Effects

Environmental

- The volcano released lots of greenhouse gases which are harmful to the atmosphere.

- Some say it benefited the environment as 95 000 flights did not take place.

- Scientists say that the volcano may just be awakening, that its previous eruption lasted for 2 years and that they are expecting many future eruptions. They say this eruption may spark the eruption of its neighbour, Mount Katla, a bigger and more powerful volcano that would cause more havoc.

- Large amounts of volcanic ash fell onto the town of Vik in Iceland.

- Areas around the volcano were flooded by the melting glacier.

- Land near to the volcano was covered in ash and this poisoned animals.

Economic

- Eurocontrol traffic control closed all airports because of the risk of ash harming aeroplane engines. Ash clouds pose a danger to aircraft and can lead to engine failure. The fine, abrasive particles erode metal, clog fuel and cooling systems and melt to form glassy deposits. Flight instruments, windows, lights, wings and cabin air supply can also be affected. However, airspace was being closed based on theoretical models, not on facts.

- After being closed for 6 days, British airspace reopened.

- 95 000 flights were cancelled and it took several weeks to clear the backlog of flights.

- Global airlines lost about £1.1bn of revenue.

- Tens of thousands of people were stranded, unable to get to work. Businesses around the world were affected.

- Producers of perishable goods, such as food and flowers, were hit hard as their goods were left at airports.

- Car maker Nissan had to suspend production for a day as it could not import components.

Social

- The volcano brought European air traffic to a standstill.

- 1.2 million passengers a day could not fly.

- Many people missed weddings, funerals or long-awaited holidays because of the halt in air transport.

- Many people who lived under flight paths enjoyed the lack of noise for a few days.

- Scientists said that the ash was travelling high in the atmosphere, was not likely to come down and if it did come down, it would be too diluted to have any affect on people in the UK.

- The World Health Organization said that falling ash was 'more bothersome than hazardous to your health'.

- Doctors advised patients with asthma, bronchitis, emphysema or heart disease (those most at risk) to remain indoors to avoid irritation to their throat and lungs, a runny nose or itchy eyes.

- Icelandic farms near to the volcano were damaged. The ash fall poisoned animals and destroyed farmers' livelihoods.

Human response

- The then UK Prime Minister, Gordon Brown, ordered three Navy ships to be sent to help stranded Brits unable to return home.

- Ryanair laid on extra flights from Spain to the UK and has now had to comply with EU rules and pay for stranded passengers' food and accommodation

- Thomas Cook sent rescue planes to Cancun, Heraklion and Sharm-el-Shake and returned 2500 passengers.

- Insurance companies refused to pay travellers extra accommodation costs or the cost of alternative journeys home as they said that this was an act of God and therefore exempt from payment. In the end most airlines paid out reasonable costs to holidaymakers.

- The emergency services in Iceland evacuated hundreds of people from the area before any water flowed downhill and dug trenches through the roads to allow floodwaters to pass without washing away bridges.

Case study 3.4 – L'Aquila earthquake, Italy (MEDC), 2009

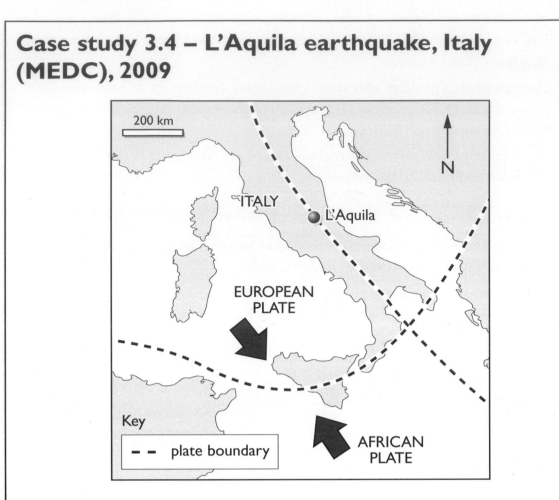

Facts

- An earthquake with a magnitude of 6.3 on the Richter scale hit on 6th April 2009.

- There had been around 100 minor tremors since the previous January and two smaller earthquakes the previous day.

- Later an aftershock of 5.3 magnitude occurred.

- The focus was 10 km below the Earth's surface.

Cause

- The Eurasian and African plates meet along a line which runs through North Africa and crosses the Mediterranean near southern Italy and Greece. As a result two main cracks (fault lines) cut across the Italian peninsula, one running north-south along the spine of the Apennine mountains and another crossing east-west south of Rome and north of Naples.

- The region surrounding L'Aquila is therefore criss-crossed by fault lines.

- The city is built on the bed of an ancient lake, which exaggerates the seismic waves.

- To the east in the Adriatic Sea, the earth's crust (a mini plate called the Adria) is subducting under Italy.

Effects

Economic

- The earthquake cost Italy $4 billion.

- Tourism in the historical city declined.

- 26 cities and towns were damaged. Poor building standards and construction materials meant that buildings collapsed easily.

- 3000 to 11 000 buildings in the medieval city were damaged. The dome on the church of St Augustine collapsed and damage was caused to the city archives.

Social

- 308 people are known to have died.

- 28 000 people were left homeless.

- The new wing of L'Aquila Hospital suffered extensive damage and was closed down.

- Schools were closed in the Abruzzo region.

- The aftershock caused safety issues for rescue crews.

Human response

- 40 000 people who were made homeless were put in tented camps and 10 000 were housed in hotels on the coast.

- All Italian mobile phone companies sent free minutes and credit to customers.

- Tax billing and mortgage payments were suspended by the government.

- Aid was offered by many counties including Austria, Brazil, Croatia, France, Germany, Spain, Greece, Switzerland, Tunisia, Ukraine and the USA.

- Prime Minister Silvio Berlusconi refused to accept foreign aid, with the exception of the United States' offer of aid for reconstruction.

- Aid was offered by various organisations, companies and celebrities, including Carla Bruni, Madonna and Fiat. This help was also declined.

Case study 3.5 – Haiti earthquake (LEDC), 2010

Facts

- The quake struck on 12th January 2010 at 4.53 p.m.

- The quake measured 7 on the Richter scale.

- The epicentre was 15 km south-west of Port-au-Prince.

- The earthquake was quickly followed by two strong aftershocks of 5.9 and 5.5 magnitude.

- Haiti forms part of the island of Hispaniola. Hispaniola contains two countries: Haiti and the Dominican Republic.

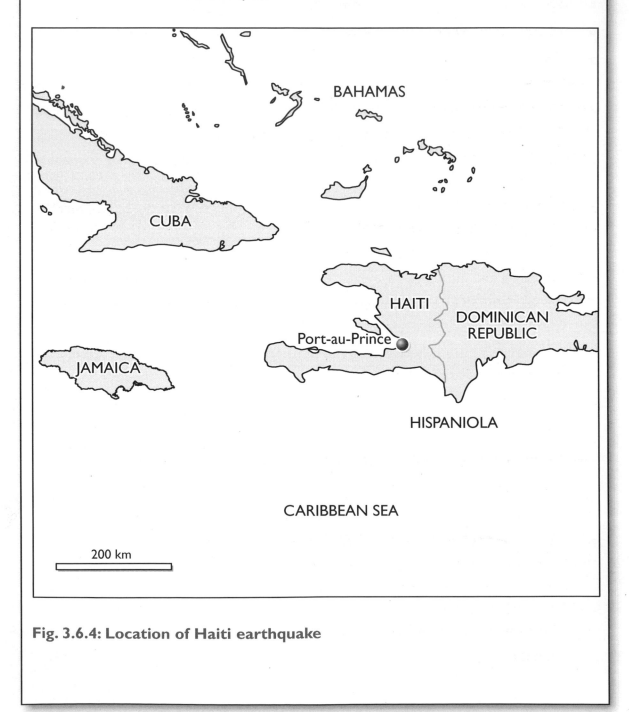

Fig. 3.6.4: Location of Haiti earthquake

Cause

- The conservative plate boundary between the Caribbean and North American plates runs right through Haiti.

- These two plates constantly slide past one another, about 2 cm/year, with the Caribbean plate moving eastward with respect to the North American plate.

- The focus of the Haiti quake was 10 km below the Earth's surface. This is very shallow, so the energy that was released was very close to the surface and caused violent ground shaking.

Effects

Social

- Haiti's government says about 230 000 people died in the earthquake.

- About 300 000 were injured.

- The survivors had nowhere to go as the hospitals were full.

- Patients were treated without proper doctors and medical equipment as the doctors had been killed or injured and the equipment had been destroyed.

- There was a lack of food meaning that even those who survived suffered extreme hunger.

- There was an acute shortage of drinking water. The water supply system, which before the disaster only provided 40% of the population of Port-au-Prince with clean water, had effectively collapsed.

- Mass graves were commissioned holding up to 7000 corpses each. The remaining bodies, which could not be buried, were used as a road block to protest against the lack of aid.

- As people tried to help their families and others, violence and looting broke out, which could not be controlled due to the lack of police.

- The high death rate was due to a number of factors: 72.1% of the population lives on less than $2 a day; the people lived in packed shanty towns in poorly constructed buildings; builders do not follow safety codes and bribes are given so that builders can take short cuts; the quake hit close to a poorly constructed, large urban area.

Economic

- The infrastructure of the capital city Port-au-Prince was completely ruined. The roads were impassable, the country's tiny airport was full of aid planes and the port was full of rubbish.

- The Presidential Palace and all other ministries collapsed, leaving parliament without a base from which to make decisions.

- Almost every house in the country fell down due to their unstable foundations.

Human response

- The UN said that £165m was pledged (£10m from the UK and a further £10m from the UN).

- The USA sent: 10 000 troops to help give aid and search for survivors, the *USS Carl Vinson*, *USS Bataan* and several amphibious vehicles to transport the aid from the carriers to the land and five helicopters.

- Indonesia sent search teams with sniffer dogs to search for survivors.

- The mountain rescue team from Devon was sent out.

- Aid agencies shipped in massive quantities of bottled water and distributed water purification tablets.

- However, most of this aid took a long time to reach those who needed it causing friction between the Haitians and aid workers.

- Many thousands of Haitians became amputees as a result of their injuries. These people will need mental health services as well as rehabilitation.

- The International Organization for Migration (IOM) tried to improve the living conditions of an estimated 692 000 people in makeshift shelters in 591 camps in Port-au-Prince.

- More than 235 000 people took advantage of the Haitian government's offer of free transportation to cities in the north and south-west.

- Haiti is likely to need billions of dollars to build new homes and government buildings in Port-au-Prince and the surrounding area, which were densely populated before the earthquake. Higher building standards will be necessary.

Sample questions

Try these sample questions, using the Soufrière Hills volcano as your case study. Answers are given at the back of the book.

Q. 3.1 Locate the case study on a world map. (1)

3.2 Why did this volcano occur? (4)

3.3 Locate two other volcanic areas on a world map. (2)

3.4 For an earthquake or a volcano that you have studied, describe the major effects that it has had on the surrounding area. (4)

3.5 Study the map on the page opposite which shows the distribution of earthquakes and volcanoes around the world. Name areas A and B. (2)

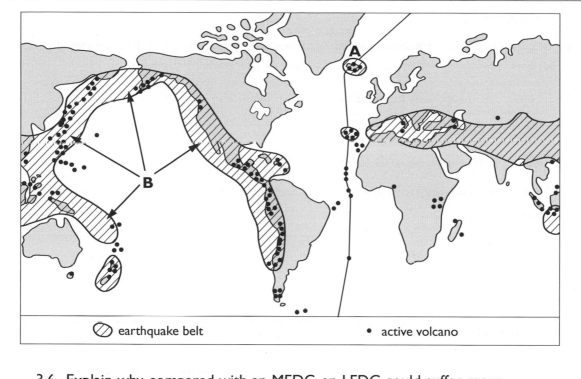

earthquake belt   •   active volcano

3.6   Explain why, compared with an MEDC, an LEDC could suffer more severely from a volcanic eruption or an earthquake.   (3)

Summary

You should now know the following:

1. The different types of plate boundaries.

2. The different types of volcanoes.

3. Why plates move.

4. How to annotate a destructive plate boundary.

5. The immediate effects of a volcanic eruption.

6. What can be done to prepare for a volcanic eruption or an earthquake.

7. The reasons why people live near volcanoes.

8. The cause and effects of and human response to one volcanic eruption and one earthquake (one must be in an LEDC and one in an MEDC).

Test yourself

Before moving on to the next chapter, make sure you can answer the following questions. The answers to questions 1–3 are at the back of the book.

1. Name the most famous destructive plate boundary.

2. Why do plates move?

3. What instrument records the change in shape of a volcano?

4. Write the definitions of these words and phrases and then ask someone to check them.

Words you need to know	Words that will be useful
collision boundary	active
conservative plate boundary	composite volcano
constructive plate boundary	cone
core	continental drift
crust	continental plate / crust
destructive plate boundary	convection currents
dormant	crater
epicentre	eruption
extinct	fold mountains
focus	inner core
foreshock	lahars
geothermal energy	magma chamber
lava	Mid-Atlantic Ridge
magma	oceanic plate / crust
mantle	outer core
plate boundary	Pacific Ring of Fire
plate tectonics	Pangea
pyroclastic flow	secondary cone
seismic wave	shield volcano
seismometer	subduction zone
tectonic plates	tiltmeter
tsunami	vent
volcanic bombs	

Chapter 4: Economic geography

4.1 Employment structure

The employment structure of a country is determined by the percentage of the workforce employed in each of the four types of activity:

- **Primary activity**, which extracts raw materials from the earth or sea, e.g. farmers, miners, fishermen or forestry workers.

- **Secondary activity**, a manufacturing industry that makes raw materials into goods, e.g. bakers, car-factory workers.

- **Tertiary activity**, a service industry that sells goods or provides a service, e.g. doctors, lawyers, bankers.

- **Quaternary activity**, a knowledge-based industry such as research and development into high-tech goods, e.g. research scientists.

A less economically developed country (LEDC) has a different employment structure to that of a more economically developed country (MEDC). In an LEDC many more people work in primary activities, as subsistence farmers or in mining or fishing. In an MEDC less people work in primary activities as farming has become mechanised and much food is imported. In a MEDC many people work in tertiary activities as the population has disposable income to spend on leisure, on services and in shops.

4.2 Location of an industry

During the last century in the UK, traditional heavy industries, e.g. iron and steel, were located next to coalfields (for power supply), raw materials and railways. But industries in the UK today are generally high-tech and tend to be far less tied with regard to their location. However, company owners still have to consider the following when deciding where to locate:

- Labour force (where the workers live)

- Relief (whether the land is suitable for building on)

- Space (whether there is space available to build on)

- Market (where the people or firms that make up the market are located)

- Leisure facilities (whether facilities such as golf courses or health spas are nearby)

- Government grants (whether the government is offering money to locate in a certain area)

- Transport (proximity to motorways, and also railways and airports)

4.3 Globalisation

Globalisation is the process by which companies, ideas and lifestyles are spreading more and more around the world. Globalisation affects what we

- eat; for example, we eat Indian and Mexican food

- wear; for example, people all around the world wear Nike trainers

- watch on TV; for example, we watch shows made in the USA, such as *The Simpsons*.

Globalisation has been helped by improvements in transport and communication. These improvements have meant that proximity to raw materials, energy supply and market are no longer as important for the location of a business. Goods can now be transported easily, energy supplies are available all over the world and markets have become global. Low labour costs have therefore become the most important factor affecting the location of a company.

Globalisation has led to the development of **transnational corporations** (TNCs) – or multinational corporations (MNCs) – which are companies with branches in many countries.

Case study 4.1 – Secondary industry in an LEDC

The PT Kukdong Intl. factory in Jawa Barat, Indonesia, is an example of a typical secondary industry in an LEDC. The factory makes sports clothes, footwear and equipment for Nike.

Nike is a transnational company.

- Nike employs 25 000 people directly and one million others are involved in making, supplying and selling goods.

- In 2010, Nike made $55.9 million profit!

- Nike sponsors Serena Williams, Pete Sampras, the French national football team and Tiger Woods. These people are seen around the world wearing Nike clothing.

Location of the factory

Nike has factories in 40 countries around the world. Clothing is mainly made in the Asia Pacific area and footwear in China, Indonesia, Vietnam and Thailand. (Just 1% of footwear is made in Italy and no clothing or footwear is made in the USA.) Nike uses this factory in an LEDC because:

- improvements in technology mean that production can be far from Nike's HQ in Oregon, USA

- Nike can pay lower wages to workers in an LEDC

- the workforce is more flexible than in MEDCs

- the factory is already there so Nike can subcontract it and not have to build a factory

- improvements in transport mean that goods can be manufactured far from the market and then flown or taken by ship to the market

- access can be gained to markets all over the world

- trade restrictions can be avoided.

Market for the goods

The goods made at this factory are sold in Nike shops, which are located mainly in southern and western Europe, also in North America and Asia (and a very few in South America and Africa). Sales are highest in Canada, USA and Europe.

How has Nike's presence affected this LEDC?

Benefits to area

- Provides jobs
- Attracts other factories to set up
- Increases Indonesia's wealth
- Provides expert managers
- Increases exports
- Increases skill of Indonesian workforce
- Improves Indonesia's roads
- Uses latest technology
- May provide healthcare benefits for workers

Problems for area

- Can cause environmental pollution
- Influences the decision of the Indonesian government
- Low wages paid to workers
- Encourages poor working conditions
- Indonesia less inclined to develop its own industries
- Workers often sacked without any notice
- Sweatshops can develop

How has Nike's use of labour in LEDCs affected MEDCs?

Benefits

- Greater profit made through cheap labour costs
- Consumers get cheaper products and greater choice
- Spreads the influence of MEDCs

Problems

- Loss of manufacturing jobs in MEDCs

Raw materials used in the factory

The factory uses the following raw materials:

- cloth for clothes
- leather for shoes and balls
- thread for sewing
- metal for zips
- buttons.

The factory system for PT Kukdong Intl. Nike factory

Inputs are the things that are needed to make the factory system work, the processes are the actions that take place and the outputs are what is achieved at the end. The linkages are what can be reused by the factory from the outputs.

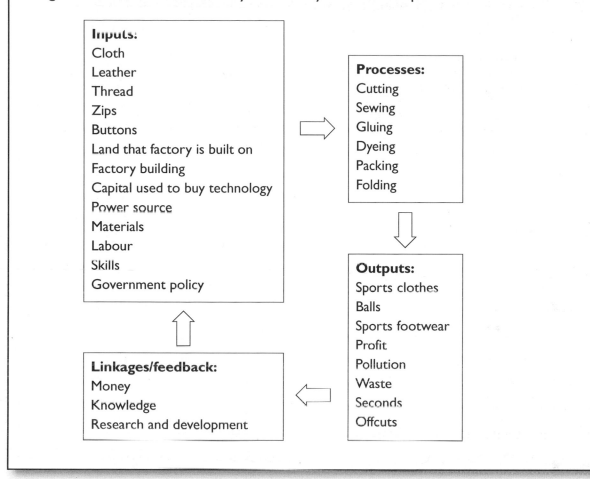

Inputs:
Cloth
Leather
Thread
Zips
Buttons
Land that factory is built on
Factory building
Capital used to buy technology
Power source
Materials
Labour
Skills
Government policy

Processes:
Cutting
Sewing
Gluing
Dyeing
Packing
Folding

Outputs:
Sports clothes
Balls
Sports footwear
Profit
Pollution
Waste
Seconds
Offcuts

Linkages/feedback:
Money
Knowledge
Research and development

You will study and perhaps visit a local primary or secondary industry as your second case study.

Sample question

Try this sample question.

Q. 4.3 Describe the inputs, processes (throughputs) and outputs of an industry you have studied. (4)

Summary

You should now know the following:

1. How the employment structure of a country is determined.

2. The decisions behind where industries decide to locate.

3. How economic activities operate in contrasting locations.

Test yourself

Before moving on to the next chapter, make sure you can answer the following questions. The answers to questions 1 and 2 are at the back of the book.

1. What is tertiary industry?

2. What is an output?

3. What are the inputs for a primary or secondary industry you have studied in an LEDC?

4. Write the definitions of these words and phrases and then ask someone to check them.

Words you need to know	Words that will be useful
globalisation	agriculture
market	arable
newly industrialised country (NIC)	economic activity
primary industry	eco-tourism
raw material	hectare
science park	Industrial Revolution
service industry	irrigation
topographical map	manufacturing industry
tourism	mining
	multi-national corporation (MNC)
	pastoral
	quaternary industry
	quota
	secondary industry
	tertiary industry
	transnational corporation (TNC)

Chapter 5: Settlement geography

5.1 Functions of a settlement

A settlement is a place where people live.

The functions of a settlement are the things that happen there. A settlement may have more than one function and these may change over time.

As well as a **residential** function, meaning that people live there, a settlement may have:

- an **industrial** function. This means that factories are located there. These now tend to be in out-of-town locations in the outer suburbs.

- a **commercial** function. This means that shopping facilities are located there. This may take the form of shopping centres, cinemas, leisure centres, etc.

- a **service** function. Services include schools, hospitals, libraries, etc.

- a **tourism** function. The kind of tourism will depend on the type of settlement.

- an **administrative** function. This means that local government has offices there, from which it runs public services.

5.2 Reasons for the site or situation of a settlement

- The **site** of a settlement is its exact physical location.

- The **situation** of a settlement is its setting in relation to surrounding features.

Most settlements grew up in ancient times, before motorways and tourism! Early settlers would have considered the following factors:

- **Relief.** Settlers would choose an area that was high enough to be safe from flooding but low enough to be sheltered from winds.

- **Transport.** Settlers would choose a site near the fording or bridging point of a river, at a crossroads (originally tracks rather than roads) or near the coast as this made travel more easy.

- **Soil.** Settlers would choose areas with deeper and more fertile soil as this is better for agriculture.

- **Water supply.** Settlers would choose a site near a river, spring or well as they needed water for cooking, cleaning and drinking.

- **Wood.** Settlers would choose to settle near woodland as they used wood for building and fuel.

- **Defence.** Settlers would choose hilltops, marshes and meander bends as these sites were easier to defend.

5.3 Settlement hierarchy

Settlements can be ranked in order – a hierarchy. The order within the hierarchy is decided by population, area, and range and number of services.

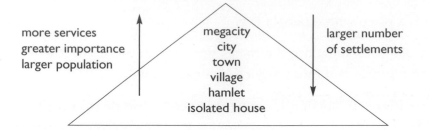

Fig. 5.3.1: The settlement hierarchy

A megacity has a population of over 10 million.

The larger the settlement, the more services it will have.

Settlement	Services
hamlet	perhaps none
village	church, public house, convenience shop (although many are disappearing), primary school
town	several shops, churches, secondary school, dentist, bank, small hospital (although fewer and fewer exist in towns)
city	cathedral, large railway station, large shopping centre, large hospital, specialist shops, museum

5.4 Settlement patterns

Settlements develop in a pattern. The main settlement patterns are:

- **linear**
- **dispersed**
- **nucleated**
- **planned**.

Many settlements contain a mixture of these shapes.

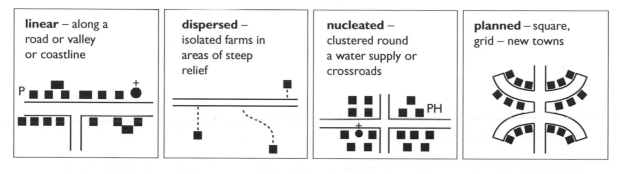

Fig. 5.4.1: Settlement patterns

Linear settlements (also known as ribbon settlements) developed as houses were built along transport routes. As transport improved in Britain in the 1920s, people could live further from work, and urban sprawl occurred together with linear settlements along new transport routes. Green belts (where planning permission is limited) were introduced to control urban sprawl.

Sample question

Try this sample question.

Q. 5.1 Describe the reasons for the location of an industry you have studied.   (3)

Summary

You should now know the following:

1. The different functions of a settlement.

2. The reasons why locations were chosen for particular settlements.

3. The settlement hierarchy and different settlement patterns.

Test yourself

Before moving on to the next chapter, make sure you can answer the following questions. The answers to questions 1 and 2 are at the back of the book.

1. Why may a settlement be in a nucleated shape?

2. Describe how the characteristics of a settlement change as you go up the settlement hierarchy.

3. Write the definitions of these words and phrases and then ask someone to check them.

Words you need to know	Words that will be useful
dispersed	business park
hierarchy	hamlet
high order settlement	low order settlement
LEDC	
linear	
MEDC	
nucleated	
retail	
rural	
settlement pattern	
site	
situation	

Chapter 6: Environmental issues

6.1 Protecting the environment

The environment is made up of:

- the **landscape**

- the **atmosphere** of an area

- the plants and animals that make that area their home (**habitat**).

The environment has been and continues to be damaged by human behaviour. It is therefore our responsibility to protect the environment for future generations by practising **sustainable development**. This means using resources or areas of land in such a way that they will not run out or be damaged for future generations. For example:

- Sustainable fishing would involve only catching breeds which are plentiful.

- Developing a school in a sustainable way would mean encouraging children to walk to school if possible, turning lights and computers off when not in use and making sure recycling was taking place.

- Sustainable tourism would be allowing tourists to visit a place to boost the economy, without causing any damage to the environment.

Stewardship means looking after resources in a sustainable way so that they exist for future generations.

Environmental problems need to be dealt with on a local, national and global scale.

- On a local scale, for example greenfield sites, country parks and conservation groups.

- On a national scale, environmental problems are the responsibility of the government. These will include The Environment Agency and National Parks.

- On a global scale, for example the issues of global warming and population control.

6.2 The purpose of National Parks in the UK

National parks were established in 1949 by the government to:

- Protect beautiful areas of countryside from development.

- Preserve ways of life for people.

- Encourage the public to enjoy outdoor pursuits and visit the countryside.

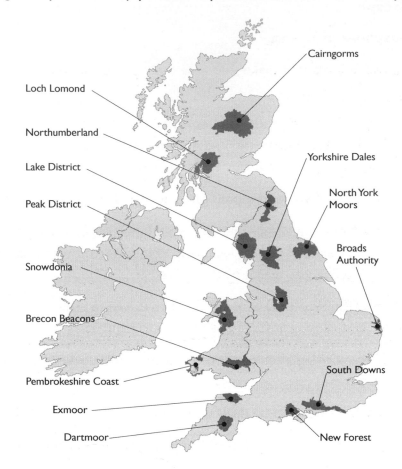

Fig. 6.2.1: National park locations in the UK

National Parks are maintained by the National Parks Authority (NPA). The land is owned by farmers, the National Trust and the Ministry of Defence.

Case study 6.1 – Management of the Yorkshire Dales

The Yorkshire Dales gained National Park status in 1954. It is located in the Pennines in the north of England in the counties of North Yorkshire and Cumbria.

You should be able to place your study area of sustainable development on a map.

Fig. 6.2.2: Yorkshire Dales National Park

Main attractions

- Limestone (karst scenery) capped with millstone grit, which forms the Yorkshire Three Peaks (formed by three mountains: Whernside, Ingleborough and Pen-y-ghent).

- Limestone scenery such as Malham Cove, White Scar Caves and Gaping Gill, which are popular sites for potholing.

- The Howgills, grassy rounded hills with deep ravines, in the west of the area.

- Drumlin fields at Ribblehead.

- Post-glacial lakes at Malham Tarn and Semerwater.

- Waterfalls such as Aysgarth Falls, Cautley Spout, High Force and Janet's Foss.

- Beautiful villages such as Malham.

- Rare flower-rich hay meadows and limestone woodland and scrub.

- Stone-built field barns and dry stone walls.

- The remains of former mineral extraction and processing sites, especially lead and lime industry remains. Many mills are left behind as imposing reminders of how the area's resources were harnessed.

- Bolton Abbey in Wharfedale.

- Named footpaths such as the Coast to Coast route, Dales Way and Pennine Way, which pass through the Dales.

Conflicts of land use

The following groups of people may come into conflict with one another over the following issues:

- Locals and tourists over the noise levels in the villages and the lack of parking spaces for residents in villages such as Malham.

- Farmers and tourists over gates being left open, trespassing and the scaring of livestock.

- The NPA and tourists over vegetation being trampled, rare plants being picked and footpaths being eroded.

- Developers and the NPA when developers wish to build houses and hotels on green field sites.

- Bird watchers (ornithologists) and other tourists or quarry companies as the excess noise may scare off the birds.

- Ministry of Defence (MOD) and tourists as certain areas are used as firing ranges and are therefore out of bounds.

- Quarry companies and tourists as the quarry creates visual pollution.

- Quarry companies and locals who may object to lorries driving through the small villages.

Sustainable development

The aim of the Yorkshire National Park Authority is to ensure that visitors use and enjoy the National Park, but also to conserve it for future generations. The management of the National Park addresses the conflicts of land use in the following ways:

- Footpath erosion and vegetation trampling – the NPA has built steps at Malham Cove; bare parts are reseeded; signs are erected.

- Traffic congestion – the NPA has created a park-and-ride system in Malham with free, guided walks for those who arrive by bus; parking restrictions have been introduced in the village.

- Disturbance of habitats, picking rare flowers – the NPA educates the public at Malham Park Information Centre.

Case study 6.2 – Management of Exmoor

Exmoor gained National Park status in 1954. It is located in the south-west of England in the counties of Devon (29%), and Somerset (71%).

> You should be able to place your study area of sustainable development on a map.

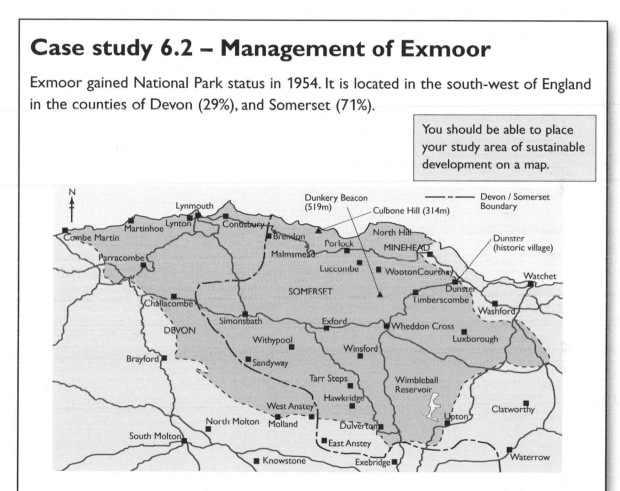

Fig. 6.2.3: Exmoor National Park

Main attractions

- Spectacular moorland, hills and valleys (area made of red sandstone).

- Many secluded bays and spectacular cliffs. Exmoor has the highest coastline in Britain (314 m above sea level at Culbone Hill).

- Stunning hills and valleys (Dunkery Beacon 519 m above sea level and the Valley of the Rocks – just west of Lynton).

- 1005 km of footpaths to hike and many mountain bike trails.

Main attractions (continued)

- 55 km of coastline (the South West Coastal path goes from Minehead to Combe Martin).

- High coastal waterfalls, e.g. Hollow Brook at Martinhoe.

- Beaches at Combe Martin and Lynmouth.

- Plant species that are found nowhere else (e.g. two species of Whitebeam trees).

- Snowdrop Valley, near Wheddon Cross (a valley full of snowdrops).

- Most extensive broad-leaf wooded valleys in Britain.

- Rare species of animal (red deer and Exmoor pony – worldwide, these ponies are rarer than the giant panda).

- National stronghold of the Heath Fritillary butterfly.

- 243 species of birds.

- Wimball Reservoir water-sports location.

- Archaeological sites such as Tarr Steps across the River Barle (a prehistoric clapper bridge) and Dunster Castle.

- Charming and historic settlements such as Dunster.

- Many Sites of Special Scientific Interest (SSSIs).

Conflicts of land use

The following groups of people may come into conflict with one another over the following issues:

- Locals and tourists over increased house prices and prices of convenience goods in shops. Also, narrow roads become congested, residents' parking spaces are taken, shops and services become more suited to tourists.

- Farmers and tourists over gates left open, trespassing and the scaring of livestock.

- The NPA and tourists over footpaths being eroded, vegetation trampled and litter dropped.

- Developers and locals and the NPA when developers wish to build hotels and second homes.

- Bird watchers (ornothologists) and mountain bikers as the noise can disturb birds.

Sustainable development

The aim of the Exmoor National Park Authority is to ensure that visitors use and enjoy the National Park, but also to conserve it for future generations. The management of the National Park addresses the conflicts of land use in the following ways:

- Building a visitor information centre at Dunster. This has helped to educate the tourists to conserve the environment. Some locals wanted a small supermarket built instead, but can appreciate the economic benefits of tourism.

- Producing a green tourism leaflet, which encourages tourists to purchase locally produced goods and explains that they should follow the country code, engage in quiet activities and walk and use public transport rather than drive. This has the effect of boosting the sales of local farm goods and conserves the environment.

- Rebuilding the paths of Exmoor. This is carried out by a group of volunteers called the Exmoor Paths Partnership. This has a positive effect on the area, as areas away from the paths are less trampled and less trespassing will occur. The locals also benefit from well-maintained paths.

- Developing other honeypot sites. This spreads out the economic benefits of tourism, but can also bring the problems associated with tourism to other parts of Exmoor.

- Creating a Park and Ride system at Snowdrop Valley. This has meant less traffic congestion on the narrow lanes and therefore less environmental pollution.

- Using conservation techniques. For example culverts (stone or wood structures running across a path to divert water to the vegetation at the side of the path) have been created on Dunkery Beacon, which help to prevent the formation of gullies. This avoids the path becoming a 'scar' that is difficult to walk on, and thus avoids the necessity of forming a new path.

- Fertilising the grass and reseeding where vegetation has been trampled. This benefits the ecosystem as vegetation can grow to bind the soil, increasing infiltration and reducing soil erosion and gully formation.

The number of visitors to Exmoor is not as high as in other National Parks. Exmoor NPA is therefore concentrating on sustainable development in the form of recreation and is focusing on eco-tourists.

Sample questions

Try these sample questions. Suggested answers are given at the back of the book.

Q. 6.1 Explain the conflicts that are occurring in an environment you have studied. (4)

6.2 Explain how an area you have studied is being sustainably developed. (6)

Summary

You should now know the following:

1. The purpose of National Parks in the UK.

2. How conflicting demands on an environment arise.

3. How and why attempts are made to plan and manage environments.

4. The effects of environmental planning and management on people and places.

Test yourself

Before moving on to the next chapter, make sure you can answer the following questions. The answers to questions 1–3 are at the back of the book.

1. What is sustainable development?

2. What is a National Park?

3. Explain why National Parks have been created in the UK.

4. Write the definitions of these words and phrases and then ask someone to check them.

Words you need to know	Words that will be useful
biodiversity	energy
decompose	honeypot site
ecosystem	National Park
eco-tourism	National Park Authority
environment	SSSI – Site of Special Scientific Interest
habitat	
landfill	
pollution	
renewable energy	
recycling	
resource	
stewardship	
sustainable	
waste	

Chapter 7: Ordnance Survey mapwork

7.1 Direction

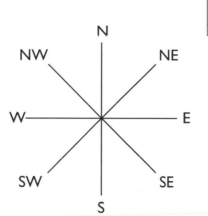

Fig. 7.1.1: Direction

The exam will ask you to state the direction that one feature lies from another. The most important word to note in the question is '*from*'. The easiest mistake to make is to travel the wrong way between the two places.

For example:

What direction is the church from the town hall?

Imagine that you are walking *from* the town hall *to* the church and not the other way around!

7.2 Grid references

The exam paper will either ask for you to give the grid reference of a feature on the map or it will give you a grid reference and ask you to find the feature at this grid reference.

If the symbol has a stick or arrow attached to it, you must take the reference from the tip of the stick or arrow.

Fig. 7.2.1: Feature with stick or arrow

You may be asked for a four figure grid reference or a six figure grid reference.

- A **four figure grid reference** refers to a whole square.

- A **six figure grid reference** refers to an exact point within the square.

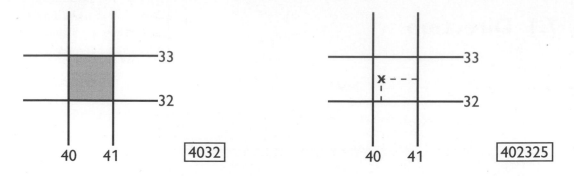

Fig. 7.2.2: Four figure grid reference   **Fig. 7.2.3: Six figure grid reference**

Always remember to look along the **eastings** first (along the bottom or top) and then up and down the **northings** (sides).

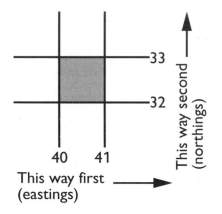

Fig. 7.2.4: Eastings and northings

7.3 Distance

Calculating distance is a fairly hard skill to master. If the question asks you for a **straight line distance**, you can use a ruler to measure in cm.

- You then need to put your ruler on the scale of the map and work out the real distance in km.

- Alternatively you can work this out mathematically, converting the cm to km.

However, usually you are asked to measure a **wiggly line distance** along a road or railway. To do this you will need a strip of paper with a straight edge or a piece of string.

- Put a 'start' mark on your strip of paper.

- Position the start mark on the starting point. (Double check the grid reference that you are given for the start.)

- Line the straight edge of your piece of paper up with the first straight section of road, put your pencil point on the end of this section, then work along the road 'twisting' the paper around your pencil point.

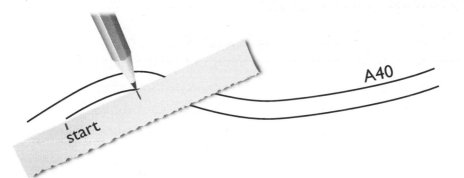

Fig. 7.3.1: Measuring a wiggly line distance

- At the 'finish' grid reference, make a mark on the paper.

- Line your piece of paper up on the scale of the map. Ensure that you start at 0 km on the scale.

- If the question asks you to calculate the distance to the nearest whole kilometre, make sure that you do this. If the question does not ask for this, calculate the distance to one decimal place.

- Remember to add the units (km) to your answer.

7.4 Area

The question will ask you to calculate the area of a large feature such as a wood or lake. You are usually given choices and have to tick the box that you think is the most likely area of the feature.

- Look carefully at how many grid squares the feature takes up.

- Each grid square has an area of 1 km².

- Imagine adding part squares together to make whole squares.

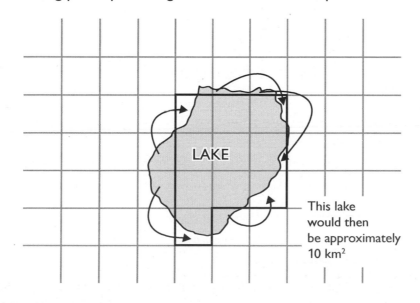

This lake would then be approximately 10 km²

Fig. 7.4.1: Calculating area

7.5 Height and relief

You may be asked to state the altitude at a certain point or the difference in altitude between two points. You have clues on the map to help you:

- **Contour lines** are brown lines on the map that join all places of equal height. Not all contour lines are labelled with a height, so you have to calculate their height by looking at the labelled contour lines or spot heights around them.

- **Spot heights** are black numbers on the map that indicate the exact height at a certain spot.

If you are asked to work out how high you have climbed if you walk from one location to another, you need to subtract the starting point height from the finishing point height.

Remember to add the units (m) to your answer.

If you are asked to describe or compare the relief in two parts of the map then you need to imagine the landscape that the contour lines are creating in 3D. Use words such as flat, undulating, hilly, mountainous, valley, plateau and ridge.

7.6 Cross-sections

You may be asked to draw something such as a road, path or woodland onto a cross-section. To do this you will need a piece of paper with a straight edge.

- Line up the straight edge of your piece of paper along the bottom axis on the cross-section that you have been given.

- Add a start mark and a finish mark on your piece of paper. Write down the grid references for the start and finish points.

- Place your piece of paper between these two grid references on the map.

- Mark onto the piece of paper where the road, path or woodland touches the paper.

- Mark on the height of the land as you move along the piece of paper.

- Then position the piece of paper back onto the cross-section and mark with an arrow or a bracket the correct location of each feature. Annotate the cross-section with the names of the features.

- Mark the height of the land on to the cross section and join up the dots to show the relief of the section covered.

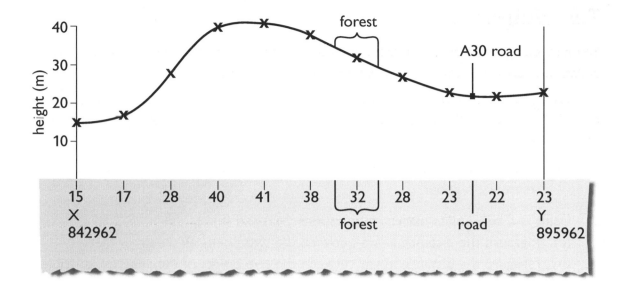

Fig. 7.6.1: Drawing a cross-section

You may also be asked to annotate simple sketch sections.

Summary

You should now know the following:

1. How to identify features at four and six figure grid references.

2. How to give four and six figure grid references for features.

3. How to calculate distance.

4. How to calculate area.

5. How to give a direction from one place to another.

6. How to estimate altitude.

7. How to describe the relief of an area.

8. How to annotate cross sections and sketch sections.

Test yourself

Before moving on to the next chapter, make sure you can answer the following questions. You will need to use an Ordnance Survey map (1:50 000 or 1:25 000).

1. (a) If the map is of your local area, find the location of either your house or your school, and write the six figure grid reference number. If the map is of a different area, choose any building or landmark.
   (b) Find an example of an industry on the map, and write the six figure grid reference number.

2. Using the two points marked in questions 1 (a) and (b):
   (a) Measure the distance in km between the two points as the crow flies.
   (b) Measure the distance in km between the two points of the shortest possible route by car.
   (c) Describe the shortest possible route by foot from point (a) to point (b).

3. Using the two points marked in questions 1 (a) and (b):
   (a) What is the bearing of point (a) from point (b)?
   (b) Draw a cross-section along a line between point (a) and point (b). Mark any significant physical features (such as roads, rivers, railway lines etc.) on the cross-section.

4. Write the definitions of these words and phrases and then ask someone to check them.

Words you need to know	Words that will be useful
compass	river
contour line	escarpment
easting	knoll
grid reference	plain
key	plateau
northing	ridge
relief	
symbol	
vegetation	

Chapter 8: Fieldwork

8.1 Fieldwork investigation

As part of the process of learning geographical skills, you will complete a fieldwork investigation. This accounts for 20% of the 13+ Common Entrance examination mark. It enables you to show those geographical skills that cannot be examined in the written papers – especially graphical skills. It is also a great deal of fun!

Your Geography teacher will probably arrange some time away from the normal school day to collect the data for your project. You may go to a field centre some distance from your school, you may go abroad or you may collect the data in your local area.

You may submit your project as a project presented as bound A4 sheets or electronically on the pro-forma provided by the examination board.

When do I complete the investigation?

You will probably be given a number of weeks in which to write up your fieldwork investigation after you have collected the data. It is best to get the majority, if not all, of the investigation done while the data collection stage is fresh in your mind. You will be given a deadline for the whole investigation to be complete. This may be broken down into deadlines for each of the sections in the project.

If you are sitting Common Entrance in February, the deadline for submission of your project to your senior school is January; if you are sitting Common Entrance in the summer, then the deadline is March.

How do I plan my investigation?

You will probably plan your investigation with your class and teacher, and will probably all set out with the same aims or question to be answered.

Your question to be answered may be in the format of a hypothesis – a statement that you are going to 'test' and will either accept or reject at the end of your project.

The suggested word limit for your project is 1000 words. Part of the skill of writing a fieldwork investigation is being concise.

Your investigation should be divided into distinct sections, and is marked as such.

Section 1 Introduction and question to be answered

You should include:

- A clearly stated question to be answered or a hypothesis.
- A reason why you think this is a suitable question to be asked.
- A brief description of the area of investigation.
- Information on the topic.
- Your geographical aims, your hypothesis.
- A prediction of the outcome based on present knowledge.

Section 2 Study area and data collection method

You should include:

- A map of the area. A hand drawn map is a good idea. If you use one from a computer make sure you annotate it. All maps should include a title, key, scale and north arrow.
- An explanation as to why this area was chosen as a suitable area for carrying out the investigation.
- An explanation of the methods that you used for collecting your data, and a justification for these methods.
- A photo of the methods used, with annotations.

Section 3 Data presentation

You should include at least two different ways of presenting your data.

- Appropriate and accurate charts, graphs, cross sections and tables can be used.
- Marks will be awarded for innovative ways of presenting your data.
- Everything must have a heading and labelling.

Section 4 Explanation, conclusion and evaluation

- For each graph, chart or table explain any patterns that emerge and any odd results (anomalies), with suggested reasons for why they occurred.
- Answer the question or confirm or reject the hypothesis that you stated at the start of the project. Give the geographical reasons for this.
- Explain the limitations of your project. Consider how could you improve what you did. Consider what might change your outcomes.
- Give references for any resources that you have used, including books, maps, software programmes and secondary resources.

8.2 Fieldwork tips

- Listen carefully to instructions and information from trip leaders and teachers.

- Ask questions on your fieldtrip, and be alert to your surroundings at all times.

- Make concise notes on your return to the field centre or your classroom, while the trip is still fresh in your mind.

- Neatness, punctuation, spelling and general presentation are all taken into account when it comes to marking.

- All work should be presented on A4 paper or scanned onto the ISEB pro-forma. Smaller or larger formats are not allowed. All maps, charts, etc. must also be presented on A4. Do not include folding maps – it is better to photocopy the relevant area and insert it on A4 paper.

- Draw some of your graphs, pie charts, tables and sketches by hand to demonstrate that you possess that skill. Contrast this by using the computer. The examiner is looking for a variety of presentation techniques.

- Use suitable coloured pencils when shading.

- Do not forget appropriate titles, keys, scales, direction and labelling.

- Always save your information on a memory stick and a hard drive.

- If in doubt about any aspect of your fieldwork investigation, ask your teacher for clarification. Remember, however, that it is your work that will be marked.

- Manage your time effectively and remember that deadlines are deadlines. A rushed job can be spotted a mile off.

- Be enthusiastic and put your skills, time and effort into your investigation and you will produce a piece of work you can be proud of.

8.3 Marking of fieldwork

The investigation is moderated by your Geography teachers and given a mark out of 20. A breakdown is shown below:

Data presentation	4
Explanation of geography	6
Quality of presentation	5
Effort	5

This mark will be added to your written exam mark (which is out of 80) to give a percentage.

This process takes a long time, as each individual investigation has to be thoroughly checked. Investigations or ISEB pro-formae and assessment forms are sent to senior schools. On the assessment form, your teacher is asked to include written information about the amount of assistance you have been given. Your teacher will be accurate and truthful when it comes to moderating and answering this question. You will also have to sign to state that it is you who has completed this work.

Test yourself

Write the definitions of these words and phrases and then ask someone to check them.

Words you need to know	Words that will be useful
fieldwork graph percentage secondary information	primary information methods results analysis justify

Location knowledge maps

The maps on the following pages show the global information you will be required to know for your exam.

Blank maps

To help you practise your skills with locating these places and features, blank maps are available as downloads from the Galore Park website: www.galorepark.co.uk

Map 1: UK, Great Britain and British Isles

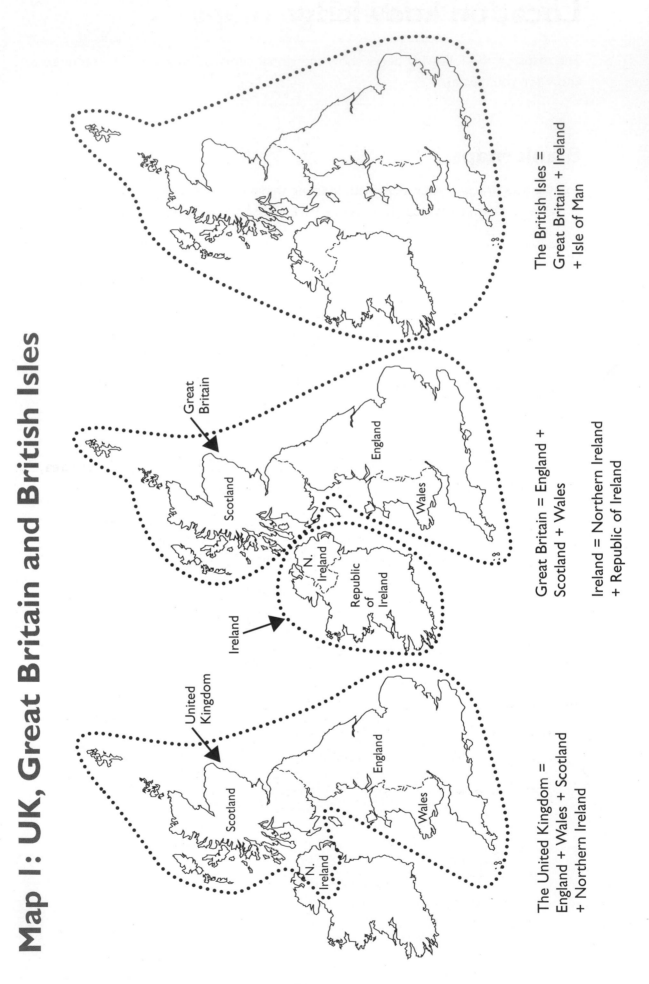

The United Kingdom =
England + Wales + Scotland
+ Northern Ireland

Great Britain = England +
Scotland + Wales

Ireland = Northern Ireland
+ Republic of Ireland

The British Isles =
Great Britain + Ireland
+ Isle of Man

United
Kingdom

Great
Britain

Ireland

Scotland

N.
Ireland

Republic
of
Ireland

England

Wales

Map 2: British Isles

SCOTLAND

North Sea

Grampians

Edinburgh

Glasgow

R. Clyde

Lake District

Newcastle upon Tyne

Pennines

N. IRELAND

Belfast

REPUBLIC OF IRELAND

Irish Sea

Liverpool

Manchester

Dublin

R. Severn

R. Trent

R. Shannon

Snowdonia

Birmingham

ENGLAND

WALES

R. Thames

Cardiff

London

0   km 100

English Channel

Map 3: Continents

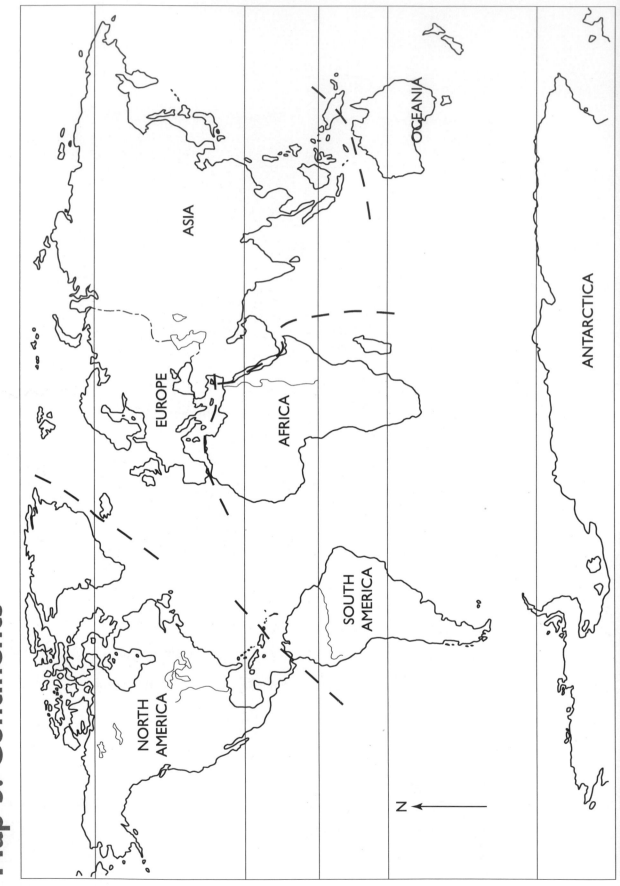

NORTH AMERICA

SOUTH AMERICA

EUROPE

AFRICA

ASIA

OCEANIA

ANTARCTICA

N

Map 4: Europe: physical geography

Arctic Ocean

Atlantic Ocean

English Channel

R. Rhine

Alps

Pyrenees

0   km   500

Map 5: The European Union: human geography

SWEDEN

IRISH
REPUBLIC
Dublin

UNITED
KINGDOM
London

Berlin

POLAND

Warsaw

GERMANY

UKRAINE

FRANCE

Paris

SWITZERLAND

ITALY

Madrid

SPAIN

Rome

GREECE

0   km   500

Map 6: Asia

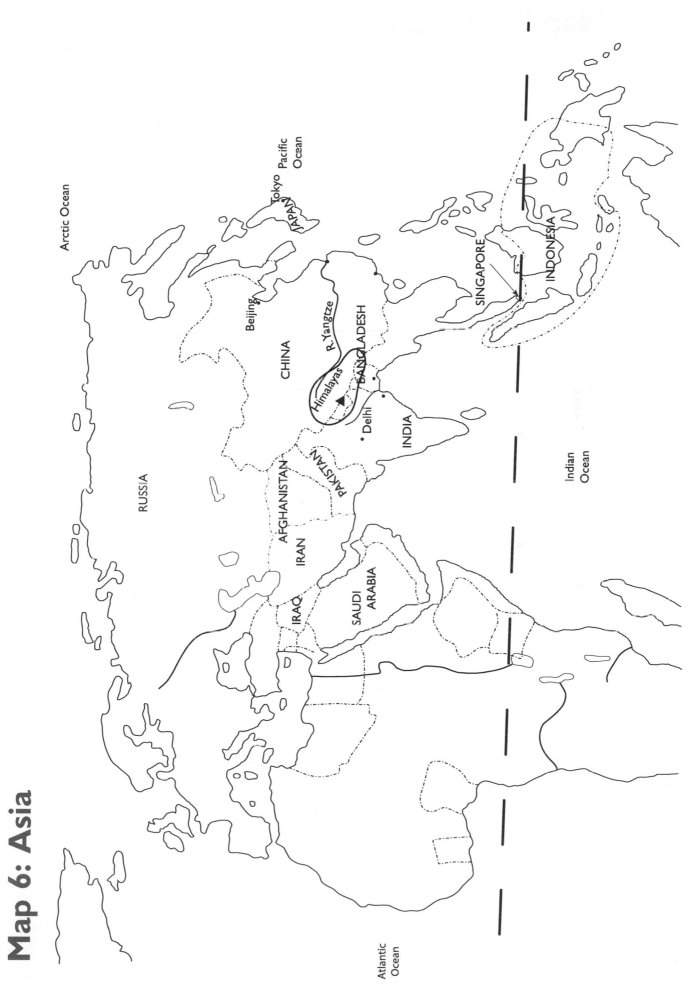

Arctic Ocean

Pacific Ocean

Tokyo

JAPAN

Beijing

CHINA

R. Yangtze

BANGLADESH

Himalayas

Delhi

INDIA

RUSSIA

AFGHANISTAN

PAKISTAN

IRAN

IRAQ

SAUDI ARABIA

SINGAPORE

INDONESIA

Indian Ocean

Atlantic Ocean

Map 7: Oceania

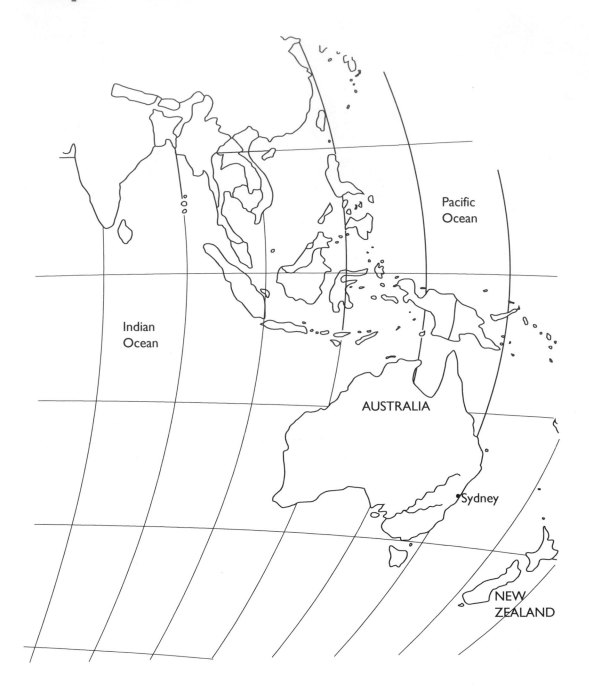

Pacific
Ocean

Indian
Ocean

AUSTRALIA

•Sydney

NEW
ZEALAND

Map 8: North and Central America

Rocky Mountains

CANADA

U.S.A.

New York
Washington D.C.

Pacific
Ocean

Los Angeles

Mississippi

MEXICO

Mexico
City

0   km   1000

Map 9: South America

Pacific
Ocean

R. Amazon

BRAZIL

Andes

CHILE

Rio de Janeiro

Atlantic
Ocean

0   km   1000

Map 10: Africa

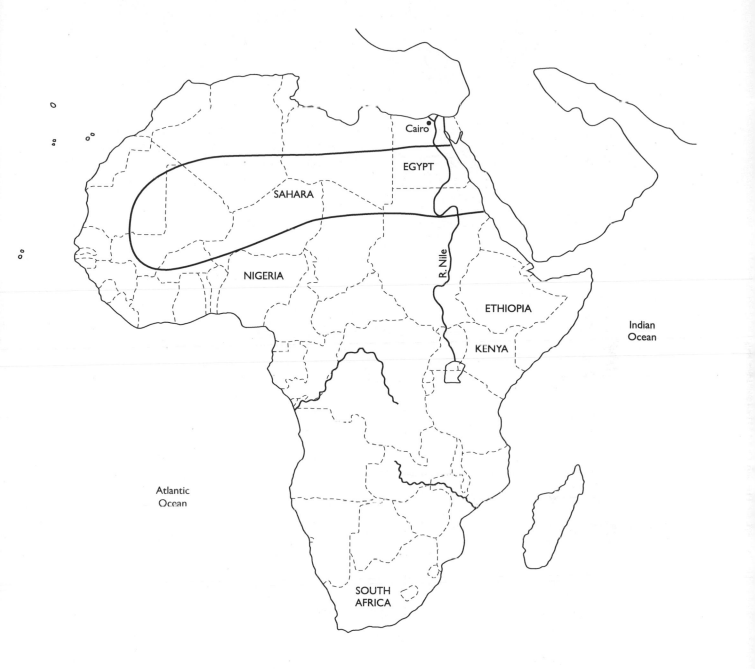

Cairo

EGYPT

SAHARA

NIGERIA

R. Nile

ETHIOPIA

KENYA

Indian
Ocean

Atlantic
Ocean

SOUTH
AFRICA

Map 11: General world features

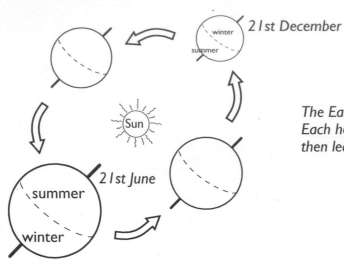

21st December

The Earth always tilts in the same direction. Each hemisphere leans towards the Sun, then leans away from it.

summer

winter

21st June

Sun

winter

summer

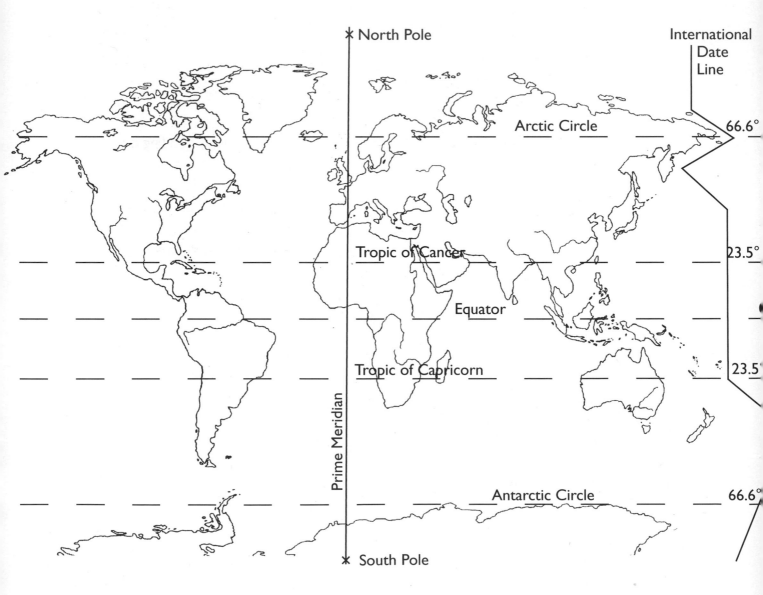

* North Pole

International Date Line

Arctic Circle

66.6°

Tropic of Cancer

23.5°

Equator

Tropic of Capricorn

23.5°

Prime Meridian

Antarctic Circle

66.6°

* South Pole

Sample question answers

Chapter 1

1.1 (b) Barometer. (1)

1.2 A humid tropical is much hotter and wetter (convectional rainfall) and does not have a seasonal pattern of temperature. (3)

1.3 Places with humid tropical climates are near the equator, therefore the sun's rays are more concentrated and they are hotter. (1)

Diagram could be included.

As humid tropical places are hotter there is rapid evaporation, which leads to convectional rainfall. (1)

Humid tropical places are on the equator and therefore they are never tilted away from or towards the sun and do not have seasonal temperatures. (1)

1.4 (c) Microclimate. (1)

1.5 Any three from: aspect; proximity to buildings; surfaces; distance from sea; whether in an urban or rural area. (3)

1.6 The local climate will vary during the course of a bright, sunny day, depending on the physical features, surfaces and aspect. If there is a lot of tarmac, this will absorb heat throughout the day and release it at night, making night-time temperatures warm. In rural valleys, cold air will sink at night, causing frosts, which will take time to warm up through the day. A south-facing slope or wall will obviously have the benefit of the sun throughout the day so temperatures will increase from the start of the day right through to evening. (4)

Chapter 2

2.1 (a) Corrosion, abrasion or attrition. (1)

   Corrosion occurs when river water (which is slightly acidic) dissolves particles of rock.

   Abrasion takes place when small pieces of material rub against the bed and banks of the river.

   Attrition occurs when particles collide and knock pieces off each other. (3)

2.2 The material transported in a river is the load. (1)

2.3 As the river channel moves through the river basin, from source to sea, the size and shape of the load alters. To start with stones roll along the bed. These stones are worn down until they become round and smooth and eventually become small particles, which 'leap-frog' along the bed. These particles become smaller and smaller until they form a suspension within the water flow, and eventually are small enough to be dissolved in the water. (3)

2.4 • Waves attack the fault by hydraulic action (sheer force of the waves hitting headland and forcing air into cracks) (1)

   • and by abrasion (load being carried by wave hitting headland) (1)
      and corrosion (acids in sea water attacking headland). (1)

   • Fault enlarged by the same three processes to form cave.

   • Cave is widened and deepened by the same processes to form an arch.

   • Undercutting, and lack of support for the arch leads to collapse, leaving a stack. (1)

   • Weathering (freeze-thaw, chemical or biological) and erosion turns the stack into a stump. (1)

2.5 • A corner in the coastline, weak currents, shallow water and longshore drift are all required for spits to form. (1)

   • The processes involved in spit formation are transportation (longshore drift) and deposition. (1)

   • Diagram required in the answer to show how longshore drift creates spits. (2)

Chapter 3

3.1 See map 8 on page 97. (1)

3.2 Any four from:

- North and South American plates met the Caribbean plate and were subducted underneath it. (1)

- This is a destructive plate boundary. (1)

- As the oceanic plates subduct the friction causes the plates to melt. (1)

- This causes excess magma which rises as it is full of gas bubbles which make it lighter than the surrounding rock. (1)

- The magma forces its way to the surface forming the Soufrière Hills volcano. (1)

This is better answered using a well-annotated (labelled) diagram like the one on page 47.

3.3 See map 11 on page 100. (2)

3.4 Soufrière Hills Volcano on Montserrat.

Any four from:

- Pyroclastic flow burned vegetation. (1)

- Ash covered two thirds of the island, (1)

- destroying agricultural land. (1)

- Coral reef and sea creatures died from the ash washed into the sea. (1)

- 60% of housing destroyed. (1)

- Hospitals/schools destroyed. (1)

3.5 A – Mid-Atlantic Ridge; B – Pacific Ring of Fire. (2)

3.6 Any three from:

- Lack of quick reaction forces to rescue people. (1)

- Poor medical care and hospitals. (1)

- Population is densely packed around a volcanic cone to benefit from the fertility of the soil. (1)

- Lack of technology and money for prediction equipment. (1)

Chapter 4

4.1 Any two from:

- Mechanisation of farming. (1)

- Imports of food from abroad, fewer farmers in UK. (1)

- Crises in farming, e.g. Foot and Mouth. (1)

- Decline in coal mining as cheaper, cleaner, more efficient fuel becomes popular. (1)

4.2 Any three from:

- School. (1)

- Hospital. (1)

- Recreation/leisure centre. (1)

- Tourist information centre. (1)

- Any tourist feature. (1)

- Golf course. (1)

Chapter 6

6.1 Exmoor.

Any four from:

- Locals and tourists will conflict as house prices and prices in shops increase, narrow roads become congested, residents' parking spaces are taken, shops and services may be more suited to tourists. (1)

- Farmers and tourists may conflict as gates are left open, trespassing occurs and livestock are scared or narrow roads become congested. (1)

- The Exmoor National Park Authority and tourists may conflict as footpaths are eroded, vegetation is trampled and litter could be dropped. (1)

- A developer may conflict with the locals and the NPA as the developer will want to make money from building hotels and 'second' homes. (1)

- Bird watchers (ornothologists) may conflict with mountain bikers as noise may disturb birds. (1)

6.2 Exmoor.

Any six from:

- Building of visitor information centre at Dunster has helped educate the tourists to conserve the environment. (1)

- Green tourism leaflet encourages tourists to purchase locally produced goods, explains that they should follow the country code, engage in quiet activities and walk and use public transport rather than drive. This has the effect of boosting the sales of local farm goods and conserves the environment, keeping the NPA and locals happy. (1)

- Exmoor Paths Partnership is a group of volunteers who rebuild the paths of Exmoor. This hopefully has a positive effect on the area, as areas away from the paths are less trampled and less trespassing will occur. The locals also benefit from well-maintained paths. (1)

- Developing other honeypot sites. This spreads out the economic benefits of tourism, although could bring the problems associated with tourism to other parts of Exmoor. (1)

- Park and Ride system at Snowdrop Valley. This affects the place in a positive way as there is less traffic congestion on the narrow lanes and therefore less environmental pollution. The locals also benefit from less congested roads. (1)

- Conservation techniques such as culverts on Dunkery Beacon. This management technique stops the formation of gullies on Dunkery Beacon which avoids the path becoming a scar and people finding it difficult to walk on and therefore creating a new path. (1)

- Fertilising of grass and reseeding where vegetation has been trampled. This benefits the ecosystem as vegetation can grow to bind the soil, increase infiltration, reducing soil erosion and gully formation. (1)

Test yourself answers

Chapter 1

1. (a) Two from:

    - latitude
    - altitude
    - prevailing wind
    - distance from sea
    - ocean currents

    (b) **Weather** is the hour-to-hour, day-to-day condition of the atmosphere (wind speed, wind direction, temperature, humidity, sunshine, type of precipitation).

    Climate is the average weather conditions for an area over a long period of time.

2. (a) Infiltration.

    (b) Surface run-off.

3. (a) Precipitation.

    (b) South-west.

    (c) An ocean current.

    (d) In winter.

    (e) Relief rainfall.

Chapter 2

1. Velocity is the **speed** of the water. Deposition is the 'dumping' of a load when the river's velocity **reduces**. Load is the material which the river **transports**. Load can be deposited by rivers at their mouth; the feature formed is called a **delta**. It is also deposited on the **inside** bend of a meander; the feature formed is called a **river beach** (or **slip-off slope**).

2.

	Upper course	Lower course
Size of load	large	fine
Shape of load	angular	smooth
Main methods of transportation	traction saltation	suspension solution

3. (a) Chemical weathering.

   (b) Freeze-thaw.

   (c) Onion-skin (exfoliation).

4. River basin – an area of land drained by a river and its tributaries.

   Watershed – the boundary of the river basin, usually marked by a ridge of high land.

   Source – the start of a river.

   Mouth – where a river meets the sea.

   Permeable – rocks that allow water to pass through.

   Impermeable – rocks that do not allow water to pass through.

   Evaporation – the loss of water to the air when the water has turned into water vapour.

   Transpiration – the loss of moisture to the air from plants.

   Through flow – the movement of water through the soil back to the sea.

   Ground water storage – water stored in rocks below the ground.

   Infiltration – the downwards movement of water through tiny pores in the soil.

   Surface run-off – the movement of water over the surface of the land back to the sea.

   River discharge – the amount of water that passes a given point at a given time, measured in cumecs.

   Load – the material that a river carries.

   Attrition – when the river's load collides and breaks into smaller pieces.

   Corrosion – a type of erosion caused by the acids in the river dissolving the rocks.

   Hydraulic action – a type of erosion caused by the force of the water breaking particles of rock from the river bank.

5. (a) Hydraulic action.

   (b) A spit.

   (c) A stack.

6. See Fig. 2.8.1 (page 26).

Chapter 3

1. The Pacific Ring of Fire.

2. Due to convection currents.

3. A tiltmeter.

Chapter 4

1. A service industry selling goods or providing a service.

2. Something that a factory produces, e.g. profit, clothes.

Chapter 5

1. In the past, people needed to live in groups as protection from invaders, so a settlement would grow up around a feature such as a spring or a crossroads, and therefore would become nucleated at that point.

2. Higher up the hierarchy a settlement has more services, for example a town has more shops than a village and a city has more schools and places of worship than a town.

Chapter 6

1. Development that uses resources in a way that means they will not run out.

2. A rural area with a rare or beautiful landscape, which needs to be protected from development. For example the Lake District.

   or

   An area containing rare plants, animals and landscapes, designated by the government as worthy of needing special conservation. For example the Lake District.

3. To protect rare plants, animals and landscapes from development. To preserve local jobs, culture and ways of life. To encourage people from urban areas to visit and enjoy the countryside.